Geomet...
Technical Drawing

Book 1

A. Yarwood

Formerly Chief Examiner in Technical Drawing
for the West Midlands Examinations Board

Formerly Chief Examiner in Graphical
Communication for the University of London
School Examinations Board

Nelson

Thomas Nelson and Sons Ltd
Nelson House   Mayfield Road
Walton-on-Thames   Surrey
KT12 5PL   UK

51 York Place
Edinburgh
EH1 3JD   UK

Thomas Nelson (Hong Kong) Ltd
Toppan Building 10/F
22A Westlands Road
Quarry Bay   Hong Kong

Thomas Nelson Australia
102 Dodds Street
South Melbourne   Victoria 3205
Australia

Nelson Canada
1120 Birchmount Road
Scarborough   Ontario
M1K 5G4   Canada

First published by Thomas Nelson and Sons Ltd 1983
NPN 9 8 7 6 5
ISBN 0-17-431300-4

Printed in Hong Kong.

Preface

This is the first of two books intended as a two-year course for pupils and students who are preparing for examinations in Technical Drawing at the age of 16+. The course has been designed from the experience resulting from the author's participation in the following educational activities: as Head of Craft, Design and Technology departments in Secondary, Grammar and Comprehensive schools; as the Chief Examiner in Technical Drawing with a C.S.E. examinations board, a Chief Examiner for Graphical Communication with a G.C.E. examinations department, a visiting moderator for Design and Craftwork with a G.C.E. examinations board, and a member of syllabus revision groups at C.S.E., Ordinary level and Advanced level resulting from these appointments; as a member of the Crafts, Applied Science and Technology (CAST) subjects committee of the Schools Council, a member of working parties of that committee, and a CAST member of the 18+ Steering Group for Technical Graphics; and as a member of the working party responsible for PD 308 (*Engineering drawing practice for schools and colleges*).

The purpose and aim of the two books has not only been to produce a course suitable for examinations. They are intended to present Technical Drawing as an interesting and educative subject. The subject should be taught as a visual medium which is used to convey technical, technological and design ideas. This medium is necessary to the smooth operation and functioning of a modern industrial and technological society. An understanding of the medium should form a necessary part of the general education in schools. To encourage the idea of the subject as a visual medium, photographs have been used to illustrate the links between the representation of the object in drawings with the objects as actually seen. Students should be encouraged to look for such links rather than to regard Technical Drawing as a series of mathematical and technical exercises.

To succeed in making accurate drawings of a good technical quality, the student should practise both reading and making drawings. To assist in achieving this aim a large number of exercises have been set in both books. Apart from the pages devoted to exercises, many of the instructional drawings may be copied as they are read. Dimensions and directions for copying these pages are given with each drawing. The text to be read with the drawings has been kept to the bare minimum needed for an understanding of the constructions used. Drawings rather than words is the rule, so that practice in reading, as well as making, drawings is given in both books.

All dimensions are in SI units which are rapidly coming into worldwide use and have now been adopted in the United Kingdom in all schools and colleges and by all examination boards. The recommendations of the British Standards Institution, as they affect the subject in their published Standards, have been adhered to as far as possible. In particular the recommendations of BS 308 *Engineering Drawing Practice* have been followed.

Free use has been made of questions from past examination papers set by Examining Boards. In copying questions from these papers, some alteration of intent may have inadvertently occurred. Many of the questions set by the Examining Boards are such that the examinee is asked to draw on, or fill in, parts of diagrams already made on the examination paper. This method is undesirable for use here because it is not advisable for a pupil to write, or draw, on the pages of textbooks of this nature. Thus dimensions have been added to some questions copied from examination papers, in order that the student using these books will be able to draw on his own answer sheets the diagrams involved.

The books are not intended to be worked through from beginning to end. Five general topics of Technical Drawing have been recognized – constructional plane geometry, solid geometry, orthographic projection, pictorial drawing and freehand sketching. Although each of these five topics has been dealt with in what is hoped is a logical sequence, the student will find his course more varied and interesting if a selection is made from each of the five general topics to be worked concurrently with the others.

Throughout both books the term 'view' has been used where many practitioners of the subject would use the word 'elevation', because it appears to convey a clearer impression of what is intended. It is also the term used in BS 308.

Acknowledgements

The author wishes to express his grateful appreciation to the following organizations for granting permission to use copyright material from their various publications.

T. S. Harrison and Sons Limited, for permission to reproduce a photograph of an English type 'clog heel' lathe tool post.

The South East Regional Examinations Board.

The Southern Regional Examinations Board.

The South Western Examinations Board.

The East Midland Regional Examinations Board.

The East-Anglian Examinations Board.

The West Midlands Examinations Board.

The North West Regional Examinations Board.

The Associated Lancashire Schools Examining Board (ALSEB).

The School Examinations Department, University of London

The Welsh Joint Education Committee.

Contents

Sizes of papers used for drawings

The International Standards Organisation (ISO) specifies an 'A' size series of papers to be used for drawings. The edge lengths of the A series of papers are given in millimetres and are based on an A0 size of area 1 square metre. Sizes A1, A2, A3, A4 and so on, smaller than A0, are obtained from the basic A0 size as shown in a diagram on this page.

All the A series papers are in the same proportions of side lengths. This proportion is short side:long side $= 1:\sqrt{2}$. These proportions are such that drawings on any A size sheet can be conveniently microfilmed on 35 mm film.

A sheet sizes

4A0 1682 mm × 2378 mm
2A0 1189 mm × 1682 mm
 A0 841 mm × 1189 mm = 1 square metre
 A1 594 mm × 841 mm
 A2 420 mm × 594 mm
 A3 297 mm × 420 mm
 A4 210 mm × 297 mm
 A5 148 mm × 210 mm
 A6 105 mm × 148 mm

Sizes A2, A3 and A4 are those most commonly used in schools for Technical Drawing. Examination boards also use these size sheets for setting examinations in Technical Drawing.

All drawings in this book are designed to fit into A2, A3 or A4 sheets.

Drawing paper should be stored flat in clean, dry drawers or boxes, in such a manner that edges and corners are not damaged and the paper is kept clean.

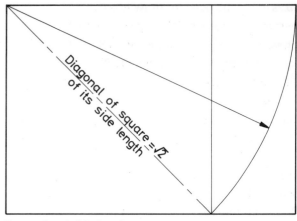

Proportions of A size sheets

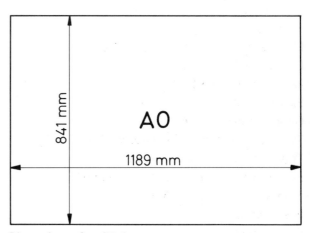

Dimensions of an A0 sheet

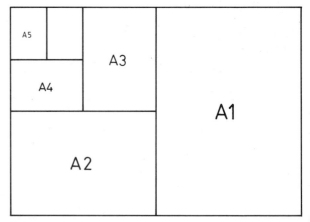

Other A sizes from A0

Instruments used in Technical Drawing

One of the photographs shows a drawing board and instruments such as a student might be using during a course in Technical Drawing. Good, clean and accurate drawings can best be achieved by the use of as good a set of instruments as can be afforded. The drawing equipment shown is:

An A2 size *drawing board* to take A2 or smaller size paper: 470 mm by 650 mm. It is made from a wood with a clean and even-textured surface.

A *Tee square.* That shown is fitted with an opaque plastic straight edge, but a wooden or a clear plastic straight edge will provide an instrument equally good.

Two *set squares*, a 200 mm 45° set square, and a 250 mm 30°, 60° set square, both made in clear plastic. Set squares are best made from a transparent material to enable work already drawn on the paper to be seen through the instrument.

A 150 mm *protractor*. This also is made from a clear, transparent plastic to enable work on the paper to be seen as it is used.

Two *pencil compasses* are advisable. The smaller compass gives a maximum radius setting of about 40 mm. The larger will draw accurate arcs up to approximately 150 mm in radius. It is advisable to use an H or HB pencil lead in the compasses, sharpened with a flat surface on one side of the lead. When the compass points are closed together the steel point should project beyond the end of the pencil point by about the thickness of the drawing paper.

A good quality *pencil eraser* should be available. Poor quality erasers can cause bad smudging on drawings.

At least two *pencils* should be available. It is suggested that a 2H pencil be used for all straight line work and an HB pencil for all freehand work and lettering. Some students may have a personal preference for a 3H or 4H pencil for straight line work and an H pencil for freehand lines. A complete range of available degrees of hardness in pencils is 9H, 8H, 7H, 6H, 5H, 4H, 3H, 2H, H, F, HB, B, 2B, 3B, 4B, 5B, 6B.

A *ruler*, marked in millimetres and made either from a plastic or from boxwood, should be part of the student's equipment.

Care of instruments

Cleanliness of instruments is very important if clean drawings are to be achieved. A clean handkerchief or duster, or a clean piece of soft paper should be kept nearby on which instruments can be cleaned as necessary.

Steel compass points must be sharpened as necessary. A blunted or broken compass point can be sharpened on a small carborundum stone.

Good quality pencils are needed to achieve good quality drawing. The 2H pencil can be sharpened to a 'chisel edge' and the HB pencil sharpened to a round point as shown in the smaller photograph. If a piece of fine glasspaper, a piece of fine emery cloth, or a small fine file is kept close at hand, it can be used for sharpening the pencil leads as they become dulled by use.

Instruments should be stored flat in clean, dry compartments in drawers, boxes or cupboards which are reasonably dustproof. Tee squares can be hung, provided the cupboard in which they are kept is clean and dry.

Many other items of equipment are available to the student if he wishes to purchase them, but good drawings of a high quality can be achieved with the minimum equipment shown and described here.

Lines, letters, figures, dimensions used in geometrical constructions

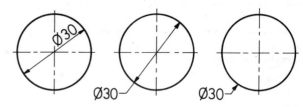

Methods of dimensioning circles

Outline line: a thick, black continuous line to show the outline of the drawing

---

Construction line: a thin, faint, grey line drawn with a sharp 2H pencil. Used to build up constructional work involved in geometry

---

Centre line: a thin, black chain line. Drawn through the centres of all circles or circular parts

```
ABCDEFGHIJKLMNOPQRSTUV
WXYZ
abcdefghijklmnopqrstuvwxyz
1234567890
ABCDEFGHIJKLMNOPQRSTUVWXYZ
abcdefghijklmnopqrstuvwxyz
1234567890
```

Types of letters and figures used in geometry

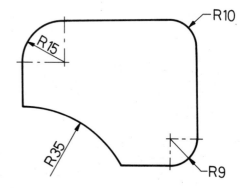

Methods of dimensioning radius curves

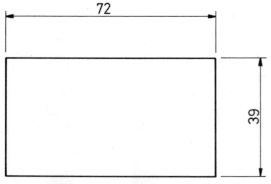

Dimension lines and dimension projection lines
Arrow heads should be approximately 3 mm long

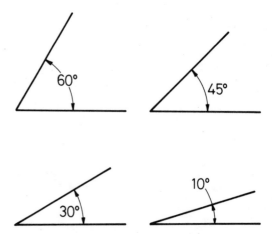

Methods of dimensioning angles

Layouts used in the geometrical pages of this book

The layouts of the pages in the geometrical sections of this book are intended to be drawn by the student on A4 sheets which have been divided as shown by any one of the four sheet layouts drawn on this page. Each of the geometry pages can be worked by the student by dividing an A4 sheet into the same number of parts as is the relevant geometrical page in the book. Always commence by drawing a border line 10 mm in from each edge of the sheet and parallel to the sheet edge. In geometrical work it is advisable to add a simple title block in the bottom right-hand corner of each worked sheet. In this title block can be printed the title of the constructions being drawn.

These layouts are only suitable when working the geometrical pages. Details of layouts of mechanical drawing are given in those parts of the book dealing with machine drawings.

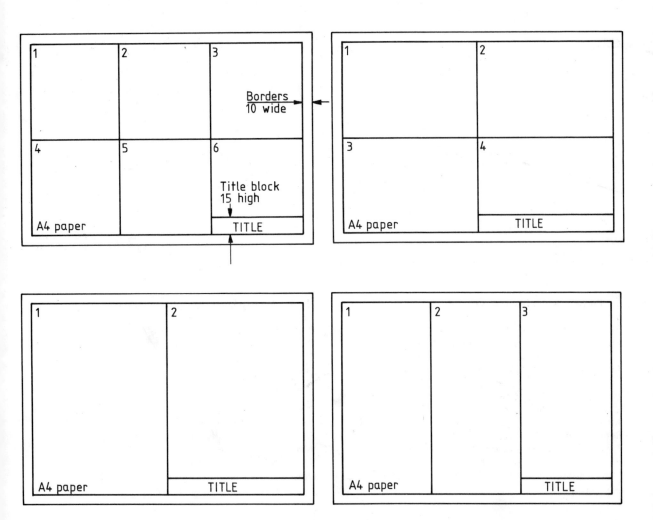

9

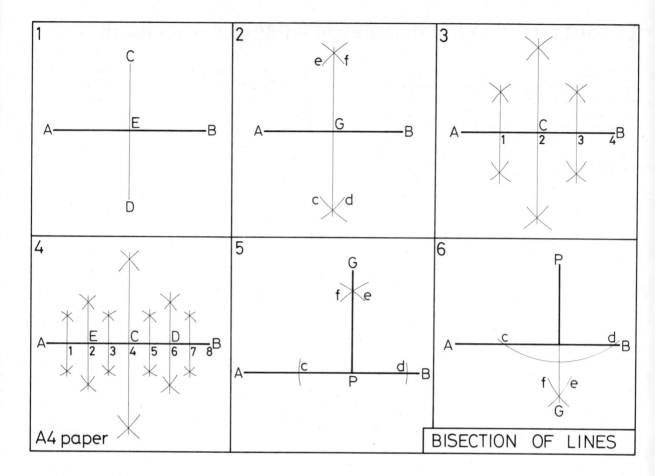

1 Perpendicular bisector of a line

Line CD is the perpendicular bisector of AB.

E is the centre of line AB.

Any one point on CD is the same distance from A as it is from B.

Angles AEC, CEB, BED and DEA are all right angles.

2 To bisect a line

AB = 63 mm.

Set compasses to approximately ¾AB.

With centre A strike arcs d and f.

With centre B strike arcs c and e.

Draw a straight line through the joins of the arcs.

AG = GB.

3 To divide a line into four equal parts

AB = 70 mm.

Bisect AB at C.

Bisect both AC and CB at 1 and 3.

Then AB is divided into four equal parts at 1, 2 and 3.

4 To divide a line into eight equal parts

AB = 75 mm.

Divide AB into four equal parts at E, C and D.

Bisect AE, EC, CD and DB in 1, 3, 5 and 7.

Then AB is divided into eight equal parts at 1, 2, 3, 4, 5, 6 and 7.

5 To construct a perpendicular at a point on a line

AB = 80 mm, BP = 30 mm.

Set compasses to any length less than BP.

With centre P strike arcs across AB at c and d.

With centres c and d strike arcs e and f.

Draw a line through the join of the arcs.

PG is perpendicular to the line AB.

6 To construct a perpendicular to a line from any point

AB = 75 mm, AP = 60 mm, BP = 45 mm.

Set compasses to any length greater than the perpendicular distance of P from AB.

With centre P strike arc cd on AB.

With centres c and d strike arcs e and f meeting in G.

Join PG.

Then PG is perpendicular to AB.

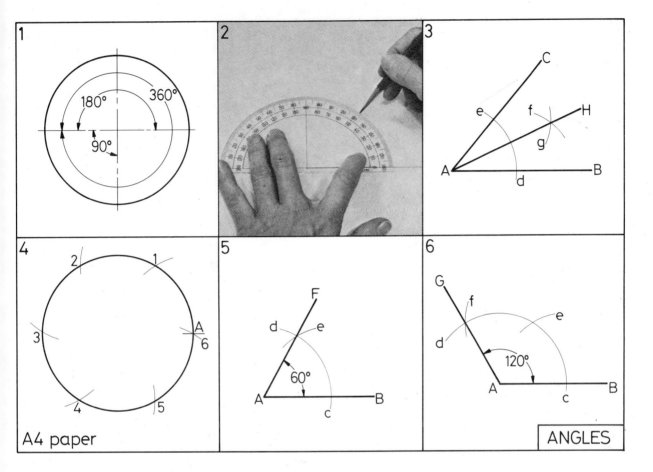

1 Angles in a circle
360 degrees in a circle.
180 degrees in a semi-circle.
90 degrees in a quarter circle (a quadrant).

2 Using a protractor
Place base line of protractor on base line of angle.
Place zero mark on protractor on end of line.
Mark angle required – in this example 49°.
Draw a line from end of line to mark.

3 To bisect an angle
AB = AC = 65 mm, angle BAC = 49°.
Set compasses to approximately 30 mm.
With centre A draw arc de crossing AB and AC.
With centres d and e draw arcs f and g.
Draw AH through the intersection of f and g.
AH is the bisector of angle BAC.
Angle BAH = Angle CAH.

4 The radius of a circle steps off six times around its circumference
Draw a circle of radius 35 mm.
Step off the radius around the circumference starting at A. The circle is divided into 6 equal parts.

5 To construct an angle of 60°
AB = 50 mm.
Set compasses to approximately 30 mm.
With centre A draw arc cd.
Without altering the compasses and with centre c draw arc e across arc cd.
Draw AF through the intersection of arcs e and cd.
Angle BAF = 60°.

6 To construct an angle of 120°
AB = 50 mm.
Set compasses to approximately 30 mm.
With centre A draw arc cd.
Without altering the compasses and with centre c draw arc e.
With centre e draw arc f.
Draw AG through the intersection of arcs f and cd.
Angle BAG = 120°.

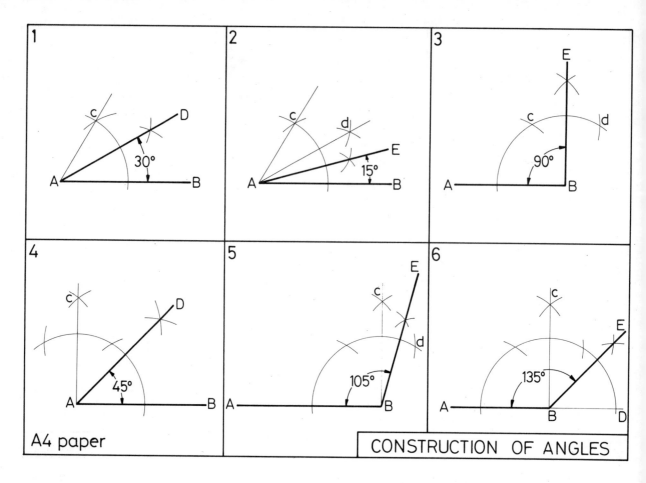

A4 paper

CONSTRUCTION OF ANGLES

1 To construct an angle of 30°
AB = 60 mm.
Construct an angle of 60° – angle BAc.
Bisect angle BAc to give angle BAD = 30°.

2 To construct an angle of 15°
AB = 60 mm.
Construct 60° angle BAc.
Bisect angle BAc to give angle BAd of 30°.
Bisect angle BAd to give angle BAE = 15°.

3 To construct an angle of 90°
AB = 50 mm.
Draw arcs c and d. These arcs are the beginning of
constructions for 60° and 120° angles at B.
Bisect the angle between c and d at E.
Angle ABE is 90° – a **right** angle.

4 To construct an angle of 45°
AB = 60 mm.
Construct an angle of 90° – angle BAc.
Bisect angle BAc to give angle BAD of 45°.

5 To construct an angle of 105°
AB = 65 mm.
Construct an angle of 120° – angle ABd.
Construct an angle of 90° – angle ABc.
Bisect the angle between 120° and 90° to give angle
ABE = 105°.

6 To construct an angle of 135°
AB = 45 mm.
Construct an angle of 90° – angle ABc.
Produce AB to D.
Bisect angle DBc to give angle ABE = 135°.

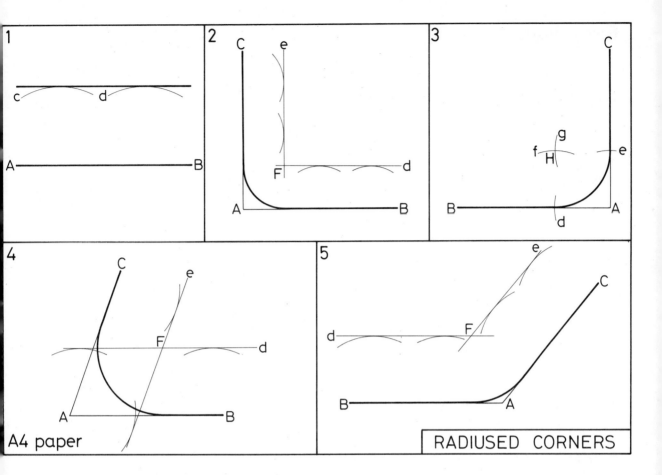

A4 paper

RADIUSED CORNERS

1   To construct a line parallel to a given line
AB = 80 mm, line required 35 mm from and parallel to AB.
Set compasses to 35 mm and with centres anywhere on AB draw arcs c and d.
Draw a line touching arcs c and d to give the required line parallel to AB.
Note: This is an approximate method suitable for technical drawings. It is **not** a strictly geometrical method.

2   To draw a radius curve joining two lines at right angles
AB = AC = 70 mm, angle BAC = 90°, radius at corner = 20 mm.
Construct lines d and e parallel to, and each 20 mm from, AB and AC.
Lines d and e meet at F.
With centre F and compasses set to 20 mm draw the radius curve.

3   Another method of drawing a radiused right-angled corner
AB = AC = 70 mm, radius at corner = 25 mm.

Set compasses to 25 mm.
With centre A draw arcs d and e on AB and AC.
With centres d and e draw arcs f and g meeting at H.
With compasses set to 25 mm and centred at H draw the required arc.

4   To construct a radius curve at an acute-angled corner
An **acute** angle is one which is **less** than 90°.
AB = AC = 70 mm, angle BAC = 70°, radius at corner = 30 mm.
Draw lines d and e parallel to and 30 mm from AB and AC.
d and e meet at F.
With compasses set to 30 mm and centred at F draw the required arc.

5   To construct a radius curve at an obtuse-angled corner
An **obtuse** angle is one which is **greater** than 90° **but less** than 180°.
AB = AC = 70 mm, angle BAC = 130°, radius = 30 mm.
Follow the same procedure as for a radius curve at an acute-angled corner.

Exercises

The solutions to any four of the exercises given on this page and page 15 opposite can be worked on one side of an A3 size drawing sheet. Both sides of two A3 sheets will be required for all sixteen solutions. All dimensions are in millimetres.

1 Draw the lines AB and CD.
Divide each line into 4 equal parts.

2 Copy the diagram.
Construct perpendiculars to AB at Q and from P and R.

3 All lines are 70 mm long.
Construct the line drawing without the aid of protractors or set squares.

4 Divide the line AB into 8 equal parts. Complete the figure using a 60° set square to obtain the sloping lines.

5 The drawing shows the blade of a fish slice. Make a scale 1:1 drawing of the fish slice. Show how you obtained the construction.

6 Make a scale 1:1 drawing of the grill shown in the drawing.
Show all construction lines.

7 BC = 80 mm, AB = 75 mm.
Construct angle ABC with a protractor.
Divide the angle into 4 equal parts by bisections.

8 AB = BC = 60 mm, angle ABC = 135°.
Construct angle ABC; bisect the angle you have constructed. Find the centres of the two 40 mm radius circles by construction.

9 Construct the ammeter dial shown, without the aid of a protractor or of set squares. Find the exact positions of divisions 1, 2 and 3 by bisections. Show all construction.

10 A dashboard speedometer dial is shown. Make a scale 1:1 copy of the dial using a geometrical construction to locate the km/h positions.

11 Construct the given figure with the aid of a Tee square, set square and compasses, showing the construction by which all radii centres are found.

1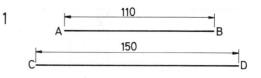

2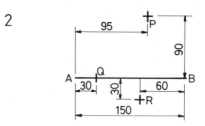

3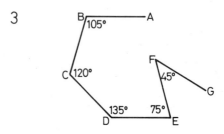

4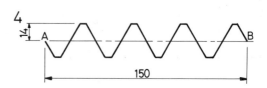

5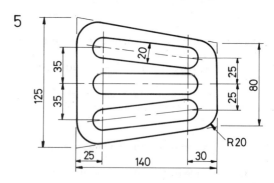

6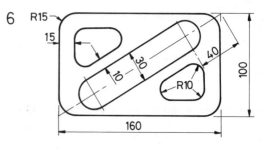

14

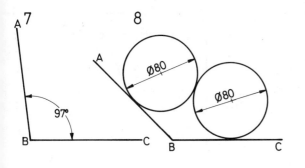

7

8

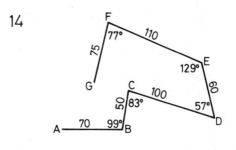

14

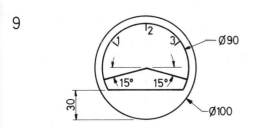

9

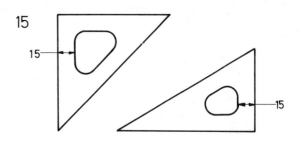

15

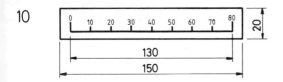

10

16

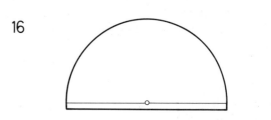

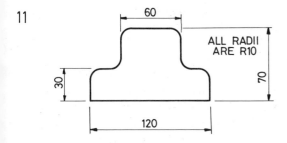

11

12 Construct the angle ABP. Construct the radius arc at the angle. From P construct a perpendicular on to AB.

13 A switch is shown. It is intended to be capable of movement to 16 equally spaced positions around the 90 mm diameter circle. Draw the circle and, without using a protractor or set squares, construct the positions of the 16 switch marks.

14 Copy the figure using a protractor to find the angles. Measure and state the distance AG.

15 45° and 30°, 60° set squares are shown. Construct a scale 1:1 drawing of the two set squares making the longest side 150 mm long in each case, and all radii equal to 10 mm.

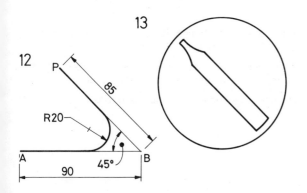

13

12

16 The drawing represents a protractor of radius 60 mm. Copy it scale 1:1. Construct the following angles on its face – 15°, 30°, 60°, 75°, 90°, 105°, 120°, 135°, 150° and 165°.

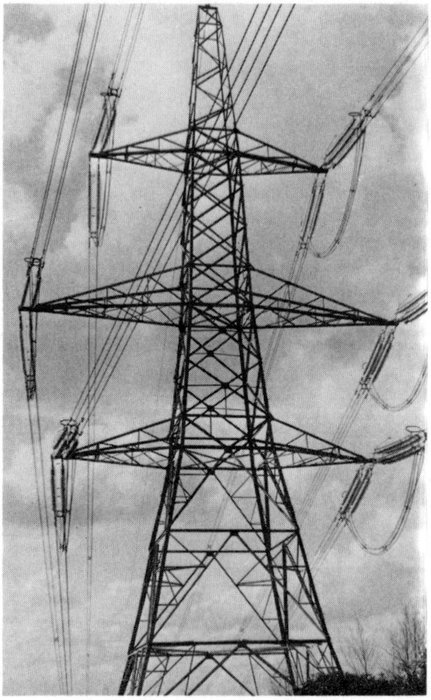

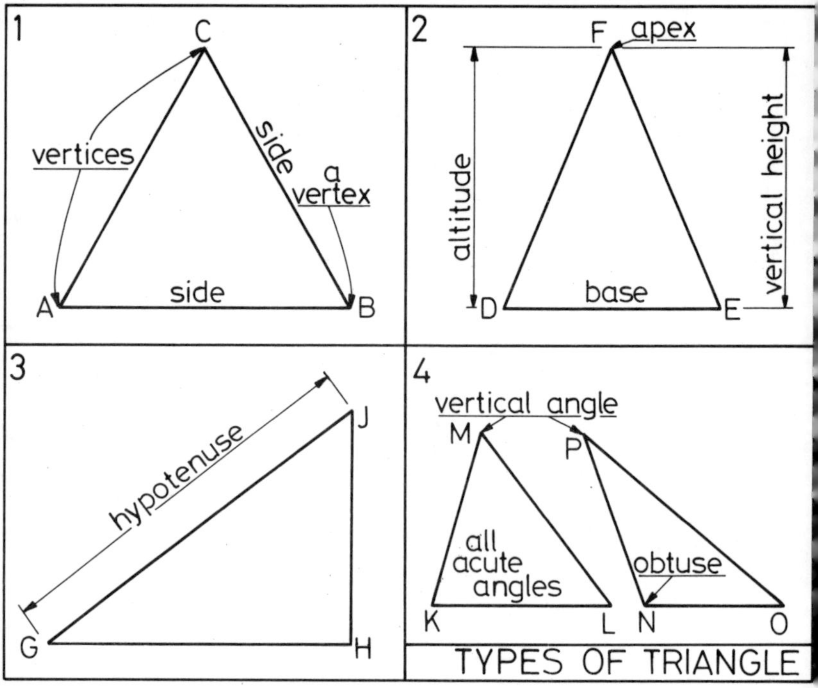

1 Equilateral triangle
All sides are of equal length.
All angles are of equal size.
Each angle = 60°.

2 Isosceles triangle
Two sides are of equal length – DF = EF.
Two angles are of equal size – angle EDF = angle DEF.
Perpendicular bisector of DE passes through F.

3 Right-angled triangle
One of the three angles is a right angle.
In the given drawing, the right angle is angle GHJ.

4 Scalene triangles
Sides are all of differing lengths.
Angles are all of differing sizes.
Triangle KLM is an **acute** triangle – all its angles are less than 90°.
Triangle NOP is an **obtuse** triangle – one of its angles is greater than 90°.

The four types of triangle are shown on this page.

Any triangle contains 3 sides and 3 angles. The addition of the degrees in the three angles always results in the sum being 180°. It is usual to letter a triangle with three consecutive letters of the alphabet.

The following terms are used in reference to triangles:

Base – In the case of the five triangles shown here the sides AB, DE, GH, KL and NO can be referred to as the bases of the triangles.

Altitude – The height of a triangle measured perpendicularly to a side.

Apex – The point formed by the arms of a triangle opposite its base.

Vertex – Any one of the points formed by an angle of a triangle. Plural – **Vertices**.

Hypotenuse – Only used to mean the side opposite to the right-angled vertex of a right-angled triangle.

Vertical angle – The angle opposite to the base.

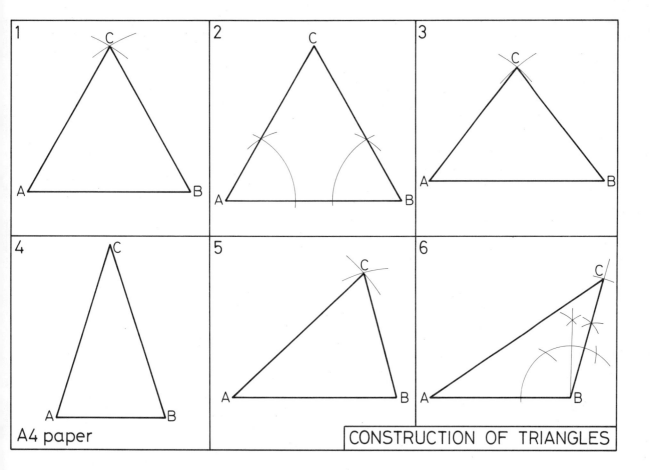

A4 paper

CONSTRUCTION OF TRIANGLES

1 To construct an equilateral triangle given side length
AB = BC = CA = 75 mm.
Draw AB.
Set compasses to 75 mm.
With centres A and B draw arcs meeting at C.
Join AC and BC.

2 To construct an equilateral triangle by constructing its angles
Sides lengths = 80 mm.
Draw AB 80 mm long.
At A and at B construct 60° angles to meet at C.
Triangle ABC is the required equilateral triangle.
Note: The angles can be drawn with the aid of a 60° set square.

3 To construct an isosceles triangle given sides lengths
AB = 80 mm, BC = CA = 65 mm.
Draw AB 80 mm long.
Set compasses to 65 mm.
With A and B as centres strike arcs to meet at C.
Join AC and BC.

4 To construct an isosceles triangle given base and base angles
AB = 50 mm, angle BAC = angle ABC = 72°.
Draw AB 60 mm long.
At A and at B construct angles of 72° with the aid of a protractor.
The two arms of the 72° angles meet at C.

5 To construct a scalene triangle given its sides lengths
AB = 75 mm, BC = 57 mm, CA = 82 mm.
Draw AB 75 mm long.
With compasses set to 57 mm and centre B draw an arc.
With compasses set to 82 mm and with centre A strike an arc crossing the first arc at C.
Join AC and BC.

6 To construct a triangle given two sides and the angle between the two sides
AB = 65 mm, BC = 55 mm, angle ABC = 105°.
Draw AB 75 mm long and at B construct the angle of 105°.
With centre B and radius 55 mm strike off length BC along arm of angle. Join AC.

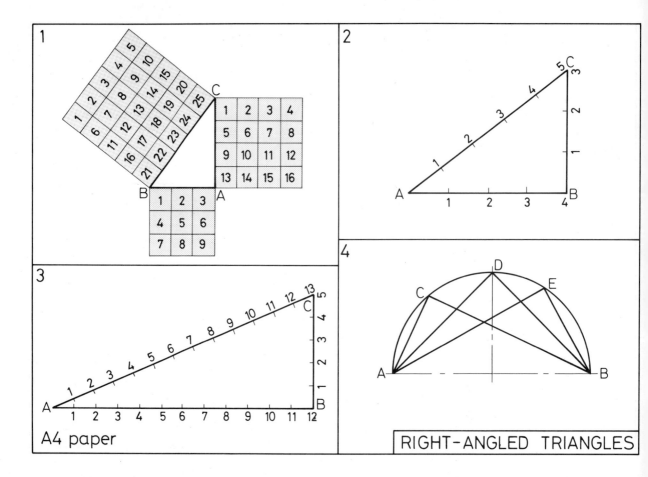

A4 paper

1 In a right-angled triangle the square on the hypotenuse is equal to the sum of the squares on the other two sides

AB = 3 cm, AC = 4 cm, BC = 5 cm.

The square on the side AB = $3 \times 3 = 9\,cm^2$.
The square on the side AC = $4 \times 4 = 16\,cm^2$.
The square on the side BC = $5 \times 5 = 25\,cm^2$.

Not only is this true of this particular right-angled triangle, but it is true for all right-angled triangles.

2 The 3:4:5 right-angled triangle

It follows from the statement above that if the sides of a triangle are in the ratio 3:4:5, then the triangle is right-angled.

AB = 72 mm, BC = 54 mm, AC = 90 mm.

Because AB = $4 \times 18 = 72$, BC = $3 \times 18 = 54$ and AC = $5 \times 18 = 90$, this triangle is right-angled.

Draw AB 72 mm long, BC 54 mm long and CA 90 mm long.

Test angle ABC with a protractor to check that it is 90°.

3 The 5:12:13 right-angled triangle

A triangle drawn in the proportion 5:12:13 is a right-angled triangle because:

$(5 \times 5) + (12 \times 12) = (13 \times 13)$
or 25 + 144 = 169.

AB = 120 mm, BC = 50 mm, CA = 130 mm.

Construct this triangle and check that angle ABC = 90°.

4 The angle within a semicircle is a right angle

Draw a semicircle of radius 45 mm.

Draw any three angles ACB, ADB, AEB.

Check with a protractor that the angles are each 90°.

18

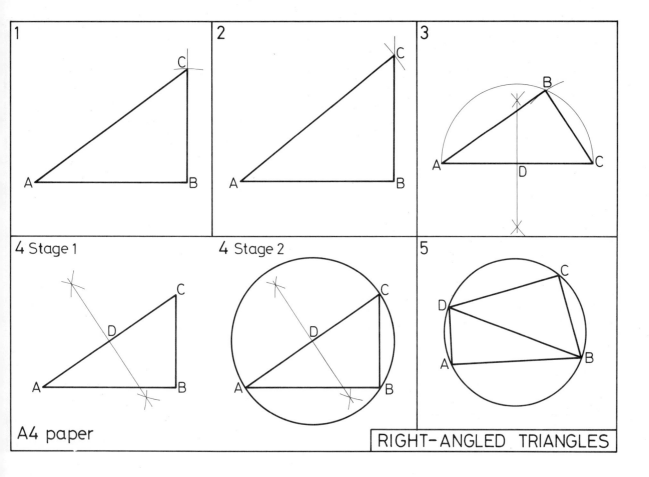

1 To construct a right-angled triangle given two sides
AB = 70 mm, BC = 50 mm, the right angle is at B.
Draw AB 70 mm long.
At B construct a right angle (set square can be used).
Measure from B the length 50 mm of BC.
Join AC to give the required triangle.

2 To construct a right-angled triangle given the base and the hypotenuse
AB = 70 mm, AC = 90 mm, right angle at B.
Draw AB 70 mm long.
At B construct a right angle (set square can be used).
Set compasses to 90 mm and with centre at A draw arc across the vertical arm of the right angle to give C.

3 To construct a right-angled triangle given the hypotenuse and one side
AC = 80 mm, BC = 40 mm, right angle at B.
Draw AC 80 mm long.
Bisect AC at D.
With compasses centred at D draw semicircle AC.
With compasses set to 40 mm and centred at C draw an arc across the semicircle to give B.
Join AB and BC to complete the triangle.

4 To draw a circle passing through the vertices of a right-angled triangle
AB = 60 mm, BC = 40 mm, right angle at B.
Construct the triangle ABC.
Bisect the hypotenuse AC to give D.
With centre D and radius DA (or DB or DC) draw a circle.
The circle will pass through A, B and C.
The circle is said to **circumscribe** the triangle.

5 Cyclic quadrilateral
If two right-angled triangles with a common hypotenuse are drawn, the resulting **quadrilateral** is said to be cyclic.
Thus ABCD is a **cyclic quadrilateral** formed from the two right-angled triangles ABD and BCD.

19

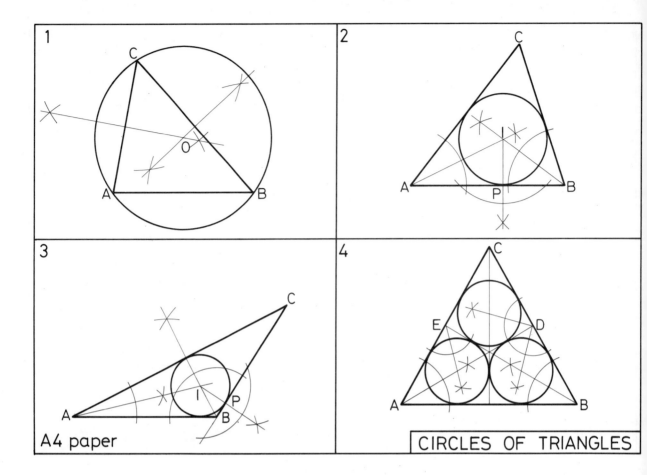

A4 paper

CIRCLES OF TRIANGLES

1 Circumscribed circle to a triangle
AB = 65 mm, BC = 80 mm, CA = 60 mm.
Construct the triangle ABC.
Bisect sides AC and BC to intersect at O.
With centre O and radius OA draw the circle.
This circle is the **circumscribed** circle to the triangle. O is the **circumcentre** of the triangle.

Note: Any two sides of the triangle can be bisected to obtain the circumcentre.
Any of the three radii OA, OB, OC can be used to draw the circle.

2 Inscribed circle to a triangle   Example 1
AB = 70 mm, BC = 65 mm, CA = 80 mm.
Construct the triangle ABC.
Bisect angles CAB and ABC to meet at I.
Construct a perpendicular IP on to side AB.
With radius IP draw a circle which touches the three sides of the triangle.
This circle is the **inscribed** circle to the triangle.
I is the **in-centre** of the triangle.

Note: Any two angles of the triangle could be bisected to obtain the in-centre.

3 Inscribed circle to a triangle   Example 2
AB = 65 mm, BC = 60 mm, CA = 110 mm.
Construct the triangle ABC.
Bisect angles CAB and ABC to meet at I.
Construct a perpendicular IP on to side BC produced.
With radius IP draw a circle which touches the three sides of the triangle.

4 To inscribe 3 equal circles within an equilateral triangle
Construct an equilateral triangle of side length = 80 mm.
Bisect each of the three angles A, B and C.
Bisect each of the angles AEB, CDA and ADB.
Where these bisectors meet the bisectors of the angles of the triangle are the three circle centres.

Exercises

The solutions to any four of the first eight of the exercises given on this page can be worked on one side of an A4 size drawing sheet. All dimensions are in millimetres.

1 Construct this triangle, using ruler and compasses only.
Name this triangle. *(South East)*

2 On the line BC construct the right-angled triangle shown. *(South East)*

3 On the line AB draw the triangle ABC.
AB—the base 80 mm long.
CA = 45 mm.
Angle CAB = 45 degrees. *(ALSEB)*

4 Do not use a protractor but answer the following:
(a) Are angles A and B equal?
(b) Give a reason for your answer. *(East Anglian, South)*

5 On AB (50 mm long) construct an isosceles triangle having a vertical height of 50 mm. *(ALSEB)*

6 Without using a set square or a protractor, construct on the given 55 mm line a triangle with base angles of 120 and 30 degrees. The construction must be clearly shown. *(East Anglian, South)*

7 On the line AB (50 mm long) draw a copy of the roof truss shown above. You must *not* use set squares or protractor. Show all contructions. *(South East)*

8 Use a suitable geometrical construction to divide the given equilateral triangle ABC into 4 equal equilateral triangles. *(ALSEB)*

1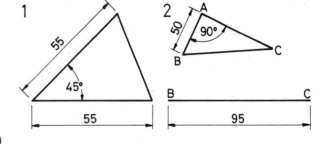

2

3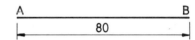

4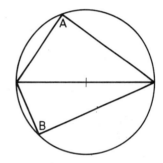

5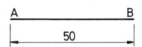

6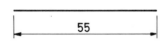

7   8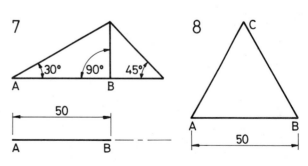

Exercises

Exercise 9 can be worked on one side of an A4 size sheet. Exercises 10 to 16 can all be worked on both sides of an A4 sheet.

9 Construct the following triangles:
(a) ABC: AB = 60 mm, BC = 50 mm, CA = 55 mm.
(b) DEF: DE = 48 mm, EF = 64 mm, FD = 80 mm.
(c) GHJ: GH = 70 mm, HJ = JG = 85 mm.
(d) KLM: KL = 55 mm, LM = 60 mm, angle at L = 90°.
Within triangles (a) and (b) construct the inscribed circles. On triangles (c) and (d) construct the circumscribed circles.

(e) construct an equilateral triangle NOP with sides 95 mm long. Draw, within the triangle and touching the sides and each other, three equal circles.

10 A small scale drawing of a roof truss is given. Make an accurate drawing of the truss without using set squares.

11 Construct this triangle. What kind of triangle is it?

12 Construct this triangle and name the type of triangle you have drawn.

13 Construct this right-angled triangle. Construct its circumscribed circle.

14 Copy this triangle. Measure its side lengths from the drawing on this page. Construct its inscribed circle.

15 Construct this figure without making use of set squares or of a protractor.

16 Construct a drawing of this bridge. The triangles are equilateral. AB is 90 mm long.

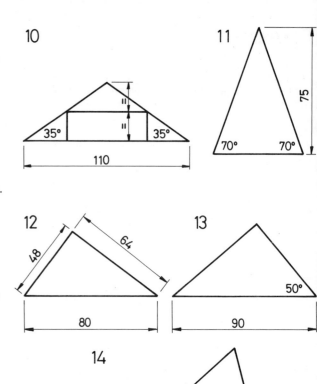

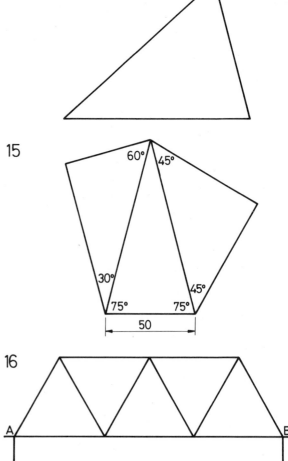

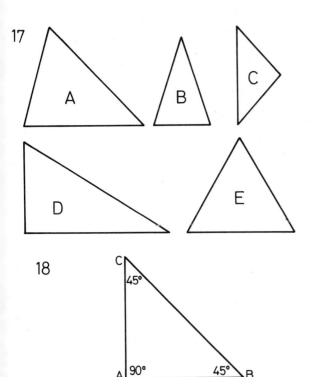

17

A

B

C

D

E

17 Name the type of each of the five triangles shown at A, B, C, D and E.

18 The triangle ABC could be given two names. State them. Which name is to be preferred?

19 State the size, in degrees, of the angle at A.

20 Draw line AB. Complete the triangle in which AC = 80 mm and angle BAC = 56°.

21 Given the line AB as a base, draw the equilateral triangle ABC.

18

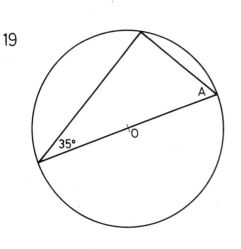

19

20

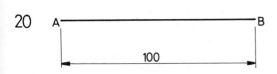

21

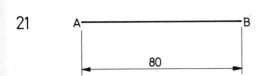

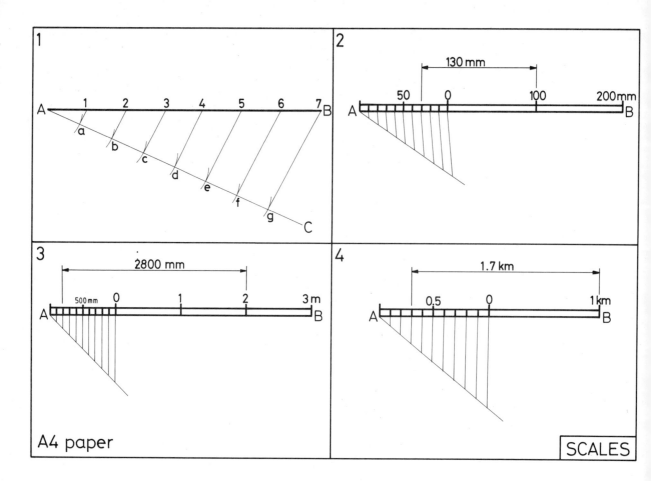

1 To divide a line into a number of equal parts

AB = 125 mm.

Draw AC at any angle to AB.

Set compasses to any convenient length.

Step off 7 equal divisions along AC from A to give a, b, c, d, e, f and g.

Join gB.

Draw lines parallel to gB from a, b, c, d, e and f to meet AB in 1, 2, 3, 4, 5 and 6.

AB is now divided into 7 equal parts.

Note: This method can be used to divide a line into any number of equal parts. To divide a line into 2, 4 or 8 parts, the method shown on page 10 may be preferred.

2 To construct a scale of 1 in 2.5

Scale to read up to 300 mm in intervals of 10 mm.

Draw AB at least 120 mm long.

Set compasses to 40 mm and step off three 40 mm divisions along AB.

At each of these divisions draw a vertical line 5 mm high.

Draw a line parallel to and 3 mm above AB.

Divide the first 40 mm division into 10 equal parts.

Number the scale as shown.

A length – 130 mm – is shown as it would be taken from the scale.

3 To construct a scale of 30 mm represents 1 m

Scale to read up to 4 m in intervals of 100 mm.

Draw AB at least 120 mm long.

Step off along AB 4 equal divisions each 30 mm apart.

Draw verticals at these division points 5 mm high and draw a line parallel to and 3 mm above AB.

Divide the first 30 mm division into 10 equal parts.

Complete the scale as shown.

A length – 2800 mm – is shown as it would be read from the scale.

4 To construct a scale of 50 mm = 1 km

Scale to read up to 2 km in intervals of 100 m.

Draw AB at least 100 mm long.

Step off along AB two 50 mm divisions.

Divide the first 50 mm division into 10 equal parts.

Complete the scale as shown.

A length – 1.7 km – is shown as it would be read from the scale.

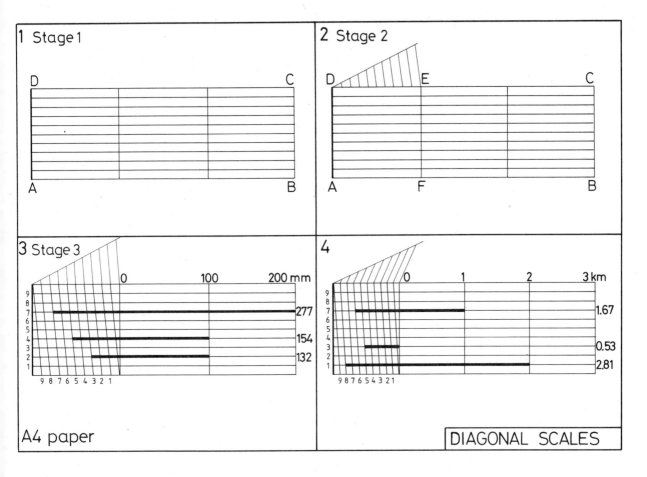

1 **To construct a scale of 1 in 2.5 to read up to 300 mm in mm: Stage 1**
Draw AB 120 mm long and step off along it from A three 40 mm divisions.
Draw verticals at each division point along AB.
Draw 10 lines parallel to and above AB, each 4 mm apart to complete the figure ABCD.

2 **To construct a scale of 1 in 2.5 to read up to 300 mm in mm: Stage 2**
Divide the first space DE into ten equal parts as shown.

3 **To construct a scale of 1 in 2.5 to measure up to 300 mm in mm: Stage 3 and last**
Join the first division from E along line ED to F.
Draw parallels to this line through the remaining 9 points of division along ED.
Number the scale as shown.

Note: Three lines are shown on the scale measuring 277 mm, 154 mm and 132 mm as they would be read from the scale.
To read the scale, the hundreds figure is taken from the figures along the top line, the tens from the figures on the bottom and the units from the figures along the left of the scale.

4 **To construct a scale of 30 mm = 1 km to read up to 4 km in divisions of 10 m**
This scale can be constructed by following the stages shown in the previous diagrams on this page.
Each km division is 30 mm, and the scale is numbered as shown.
Three dimensions are shown on the scale, 1.67 km, 0.53 km and 2.81 km, as they would be read from the scale.

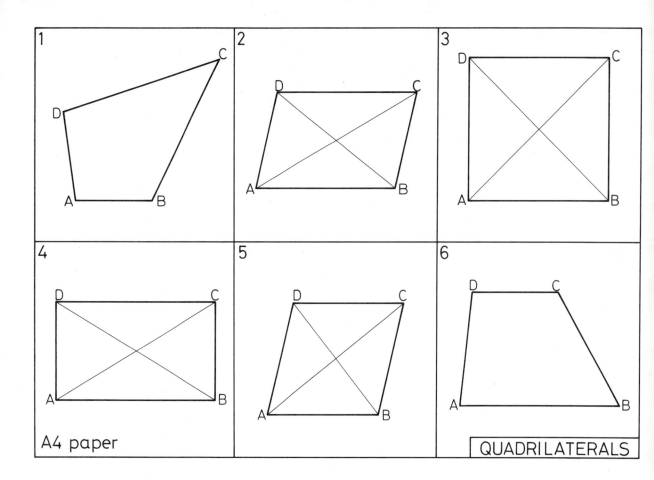

A4 paper

QUADRILATERALS

1 **Irregular quadrilateral**
4 sides and 4 angles.
Sides of differing lengths.
Angles of differing sizes.

2 **Parallelogram**
4 sides and 4 angles.
Each pair of opposite sides is parallel – CD is parallel to
AB; BC is parallel to AD.
Opposite sides are of equal length – CD = AB, BC = AD.
Opposite angles are equal – angle at C = angle at A, angle
at D = angle at B.
Angles on the same side add up to 180° – angle at A plus
angle at B = 180°, angle at A plus angle at D = 180°, and
so on.
Diagonals bisect each other – BD bisects AC and AC
bisects BD, but not at right angles.

3 **Square**
A special form of parallelogram.
4 sides and 4 angles.
All sides are the same length.
All angles are right angles.
Diagonals are of equal length.
Diagonals bisect each other at right angles.

4 **Rectangle**
A special form of parallelogram.
4 sides and 4 angles.
All angles are right angles.
Opposite sides are of equal length – CD = AB, BC = AD.
Diagonals bisect each other, but not at right angles.

5 **Rhombus**
A special form of parallelogram.
4 sides and 4 angles.
All sides are of equal length.
Opposite angles are equal – angle at C = angle at A, angle
at D = angle at B.
Diagonals bisect each other at right angles.

6 **Trapezium**
4 sides and 4 angles.
One pair of opposite sides is parallel – CD is parallel to
AB, but BC is not parallel to AD.

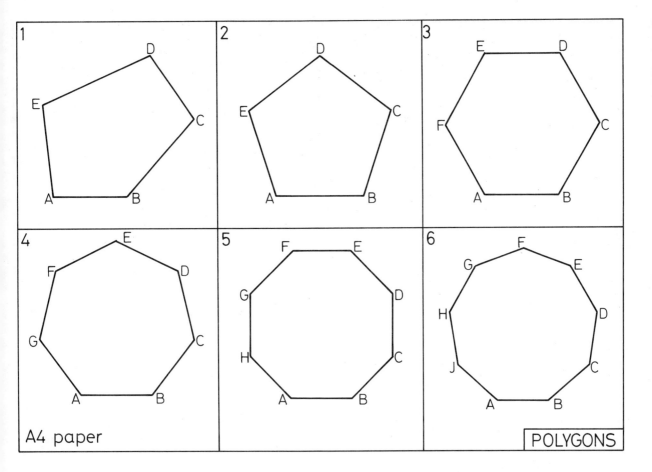

A4 paper

POLYGONS

1 An irregular polygon

This irregular polygon is pentagonal – it possesses 5 sides. Irregular polygons may have any number of sides.
All sides are straight lines.
Sides are of differing lengths.
Angles are of differing sizes.

2 A regular pentagon

A regular polygon with 5 sides and 5 angles.
All sides are the same length.
All angles are the same size – 108°.

3 A regular hexagon

A regular polygon with 6 sides and 6 angles.
All sides are the same length.
All angles are the same size – 120°.

4 A regular heptagon

A regular polygon with 7 sides and 7 angles.

5 A regular octagon

A regular polygon of 8 sides and 8 angles.
All sides are the same length.
All angles are the same size – 135°.

6 A regular nonagon

A regular polygon of 9 sides.

Notes
Irregular polygons
At least 4 sides and 4 angles.
Usually differing side lengths and differing angles.
May occur with same side lengths but then angles will not be the same.
May occur with all angles of the same size, but then sides will be of different lengths.

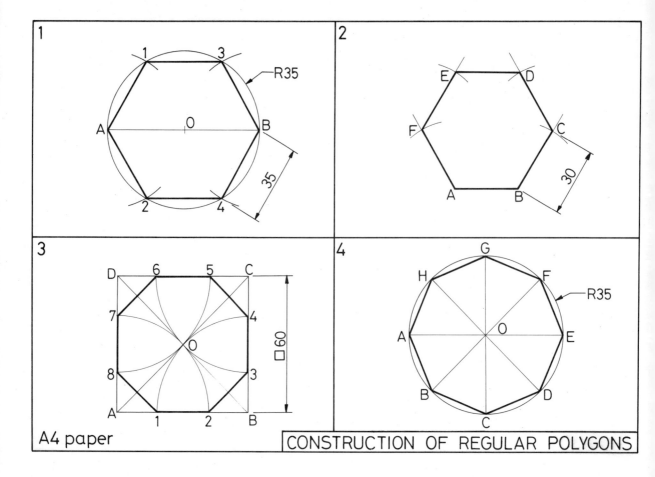

CONSTRUCTION OF REGULAR POLYGONS

1 To construct a regular hexagon given side length
Side length = 35 mm.
With compasses set to 35 mm draw a circle of centre O.
Draw diameter AOB.
With compasses still set at 35 mm and centre first at A,
then at B, draw arcs on the circle at 1, 2, 3 and 4.
Complete the hexagon as shown.

Note: If the hexagon is required with two vertical sides,
commence with a vertical diameter through centre O.

**2 To construct a regular hexagon given side length.
Another method**
Side length = 30 mm.
Draw AB 30 mm long.
Draw 120° angles at A and at B using a 60° set square.
Set compasses to 30 mm and step off this length from A
and B to obtain F and C.
Draw angles of 120° at F and C with 60° set square.
Step off 30 mm with compasses to obtain E and D.
Complete the hexagon as shown.

3 To construct a regular octagon within a square
Construct a square ABCD of side length = 60 mm.
Draw the diagonals AC and BD meeting at O.
With compasses set to AO draw arcs with A, B, C and D as
centres to obtain points 1 to 8 on the sides of the square.
Complete the octagon as shown.

4 To construct an octagon within a given circle
Circle radius = 35 mm.
Draw the circle of centre O.
Draw 4 diagonals each at 45° to each other with the aid of
a 45° set square to give points A to H on the circle.
Join the points so obtained to complete the octagon.

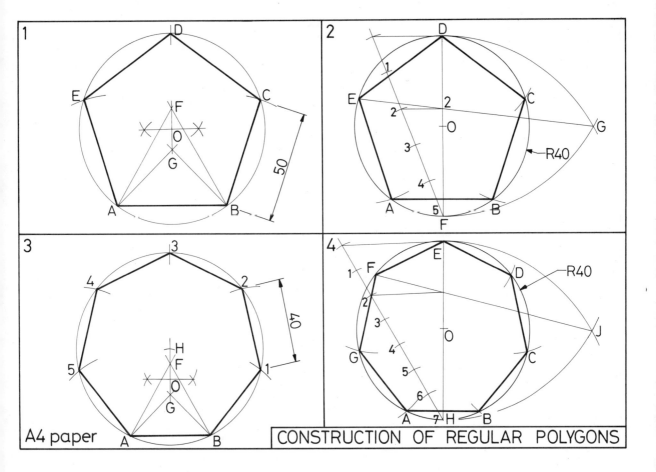

1 To construct a regular pentagon given side length

Side length = 50 mm.

Draw AB 50 mm long.

Both at A and at B draw angles of 60° and 45° to meet at F and G.

Join FG and bisect at O.

With centre O and radius OA (or OB) draw a circle.

With compasses set to AB draw from A and B arcs to obtain E and C.

Produce GF to meet the circle at D.

Join BC, CD, DE and EA to obtain the regular pentagon.

2 To construct a regular pentagon within a given circle

Circle of radius 40 mm and centre O.

Draw a diameter and divide it into 5 equal parts.

With compasses set to the diameter and with centres at the ends of the diameter D and F draw arcs to meet at G.

Join G to the ⅖ mark along the diameter DF and produce to meet the circle at E.

Then DE is a side length of the required regular pentagon.

3 To draw a regular heptagon given side length

Side length 40 mm.

Draw AB 40 mm long.

Follow the same procedure as given for the regular pentagon in Space 1 up to the stage of obtaining the three points F, G and O.

Produce the line GF and mark on the line from F a distance equal to OF to give H.

With compasses set to HA (or HB) draw a circle of centre H.

With compasses set to AB mark points 1, 2, 3, 4 and 5 and complete the regular heptagon as shown.

4 To draw a regular heptagon within a given circle

Circle of radius 40 mm and centre O.

Draw a diameter EH and divide into 7 equal parts.

To complete the regular heptagon now follow the same procedure as given in Space 2 for the regular pentagon within a circle.

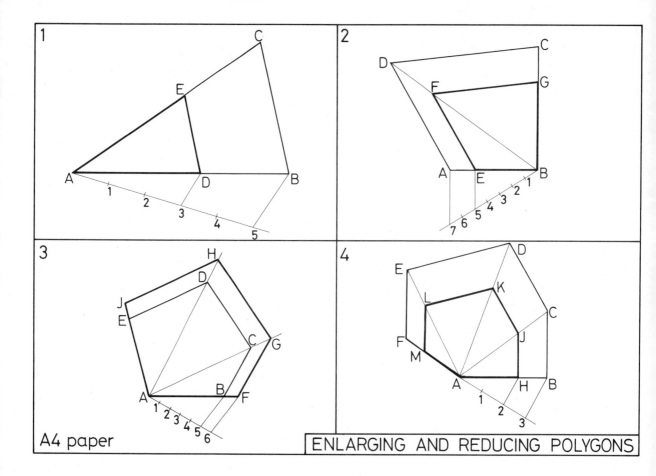

ENLARGING AND REDUCING POLYGONS

1 Reducing a triangle in a given ratio of side lengths

In triangle ABC, AB = 100 mm, BC = 60 mm,
CA = 105 mm.
To construct a triangle with sides each ⅗ of the sides of
triangle ABC:
Divide side AB into 5 equal parts and take 3 of the 5 parts
as the side AD of the required triangle.
Draw DE parallel to BC.
Then ADE is the required triangle.

2 Reducing a quadrilateral in a given ratio of side lengths

AB = 40 mm, angle ABC = 90°,
BC = 55 mm, angle BAD = 120°,
AD = 55 mm.
To construct a quadrilateral similar to ABCD with sides in
a ratio of 5:7:
Find BE, which is ⁵⁄₇ of BA.
Draw the diagonal BD.
Draw EF parallel to AD.
Draw FG parallel to DC.
Then BEFG is the required quadrilateral.

3 Enlarging a polygon in a given ratio of side lengths

In pentagon ABCDE,
AB = 35 mm, angle ABC = 120°,
BC = 25 mm, angle BAE = 105°,

AE = 35 mm, DE = 40 mm,
CD = 35 mm.
To construct a similar pentagon of sides ratio 6:5:
Divide side AB into 5 equal parts.
Produce AB to F so that BF is ⅕ of AB, making
AF:AB = 6:5.
Draw diagonals AC and AD and produce each of them.
Produce AE.
Draw FG parallel to BC, GH parallel to CD, HJ parallel to
DE.
Then AFGHJ is the required pentagon.

Note: This method can be used either to reduce or to enlarge any
polygon. The method relies upon being able to divide a polygon
into a number of triangles by drawing appropriate diagonals in
the polygon.

4 To reduce a hexagon by a sides ratio of 2:3

In hexagon ABCDEF, AB = 40 mm, BC = 30 mm,
AF = 30 mm, angle at B = 90°, angle at A = 145°,
CD = 35 mm, EF = 30 mm, angle at C = 150°, angle at
F = 125°.
Find AH ⅔ of AB.
Draw the three diagonals AC, AD and AE.
Draw HJ parallel to BC, JK parallel to CD, KL parallel to
DE and LM parallel to EF.
Then AHJKLM is the required hexagon.

Exercises

Solutions to Exercise 1 can be all drawn on both sides of an A4 size drawing sheet.

1 (**a**) Construct a scale of 1 in 5 to read up to 0.75 m in cm.

(**b**) A length on a drawing is dimensioned as 15 mm. Its actual length is 25 mm. Construct a scale which could be used on the drawing to read in mm up to 100 mm.

(**c**) Construct a diagonal scale of 25 mm to 1 km to measure a maximum length of 5 km. The smallest dimension required on the scale is 0.01 km. Show the following two measurements on your scale: 4.75 km, 2.38 km.

(**d**) Construct a regular pentagon of side length 55 mm. Enlarge the pentagon by a scale of 1.5:1.

(**e**) Draw 2 circles each of 74 mm diameter. In the first circle construct an inscribed regular octagon. In the second, construct an inscribed regular pentagon.

Solutions to Exercises 2, 3, 4 and 5 can all be drawn on both sides of an A4 size drawing sheet.

2 Rivet holes have to be drilled in a metal plate as shown by the crosses in the diagram. Draw the plate full size and find by construction the position of the rivet holes. Your construction lines must be visible. You may use set squares. (*South East*)

3 Construct the rectangle shown in the larger diagram. Within the rectangle draw, in the ratio shown, the exact heights of the drawers. Set squares may be used. (*South East*)

4 Complete the diagonal scale of 30 mm representing 25 mm, the outline of which is given, to read down to mm and 0.1 mm. Show *all* construction and add titles. (*East Anglian, South*)

5 Complete the uncompleted scale of 2.5:1 to read to 0.1 mm. Mark two points, A and B, on it 37.4 mm apart. (*ALSEB*)

2

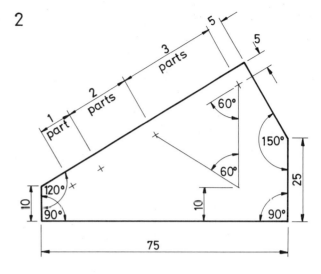

3

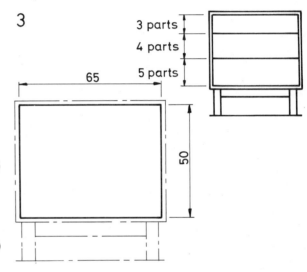

4

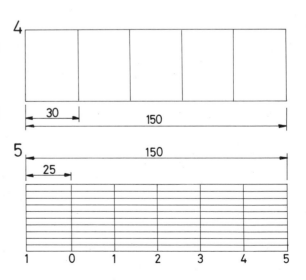

Exercises

6 The given drawing shows a six-pointed star based on a regular hexagon of side length AB = 50 mm. Using a ruler and a compass construct an accurate drawing of the star.

7 The given drawing shows a regular pentagon circumscribed by a circle of 90 mm diameter. Draw the circle and construct within it the regular pentagon.

8 A common geometrical construction is given, but it is not complete.
　(a) Complete it.
　(b) Name the figure constructed.
(East Anglian, South)

Take dimensions from the given drawing and copy the figure scale 2:1.

9 Enlarge the given square so that AB is increased in proportion as 3:4. *(East Anglian, South)*

10 Showing all construction draw the given figure.

11 The drawing represents one part of a pair of rising butt hinges before being shaped.
　(a) Reduce the drawing in a ratio of 1:2.
　(b) measure and fully dimension your answer.
(Welsh)

12 The outline of a pottery template is shown. It is made from a 95 mm disc having three sides of a regular five-sided polygon cut from it as shown. Draw the template scale 1:1, showing *all* construction.
(East Anglian, North)

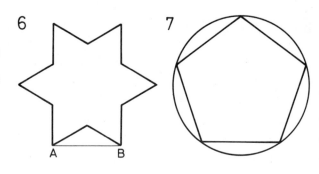

6　7

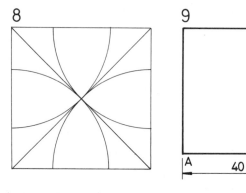

8

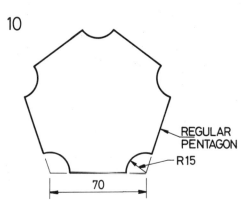

9

A　40　B

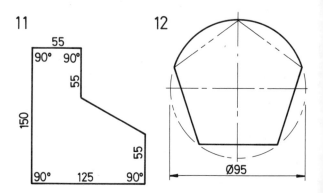

10

REGULAR PENTAGON

R15

70

11　12

55

90°　90°

55

150

90°　125　90°

55

Ø95

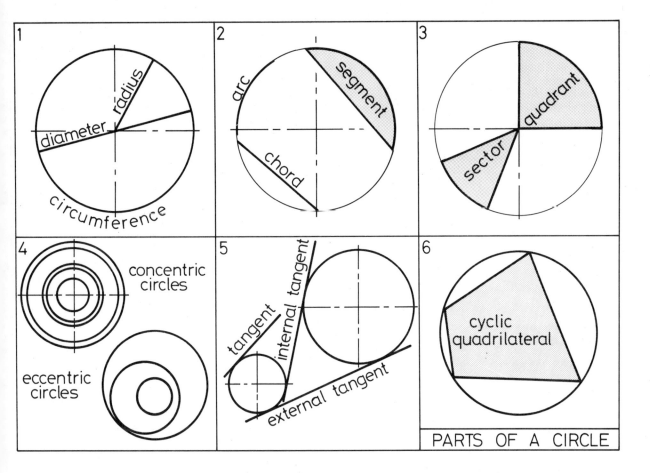

PARTS OF A CIRCLE

1 Radius: shortest distance between centre and line of circle. Plural – radii.
Diameter: Any straight line passing through the circle centre and touching its circumference at both ends. All diameters of any one circle are equal in length and are twice the length of any radius.
Circumference: the line of the circle. Its length divided by the circle diameter gives the quantity known as π (pi).
π = approximately 3·14 = approximately 3½.

2 Arc: part of the circumference of a circle.
Chord: the straight line joining the ends of an arc.
Segment: that part of a circle enclosed by an arc and its chord.

3 Sector: any part of a circle enclosed by two radii and the part of the circle's circumference between the two radii.
Quadrant: a sector in which the two radii are at an angle of 90° to each other – a quarter of a circle.
Semicircle: a sector formed by a diameter and the arc joining the ends of the diameter.

4 Concentric circles: circles of different radii but with a common centre.
Eccentric circles: circles within each other with different centres.

5 Tangent: any line which touches a circle at a point. At the point of tangency a straight line tangent is at right angles to the radius.
External tangent: a tangent touching two circles and outside the line joining the centres of the circles.
Internal tangent: a tangent touching two circles and crossing the line joining the centres of the circles.

6 Cyclic quadrilateral: a quadrilateral which can be circumscribed by a circle.

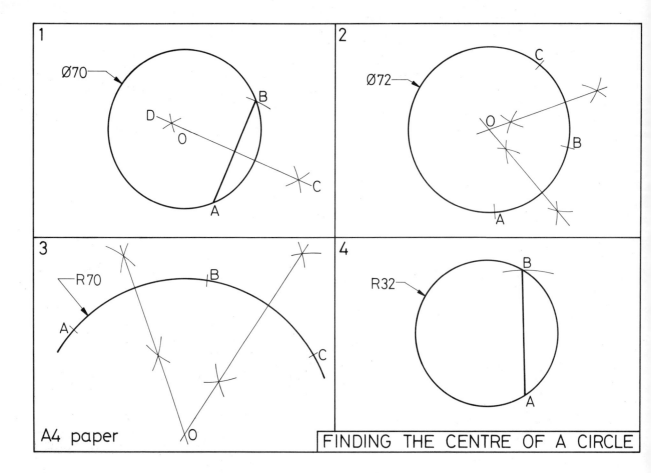

1 **The perpendicular bisector of an arc or of a chord passes through the centre of the circle of which the arc is part**

Draw a circle of diameter 70 mm.
Draw the chord AB 50 mm long. Set compasses to 50 mm, select any point A on the circumference, draw arc B with centre A. Join AB.
Bisect AB to give CD.
The perpendicular bisector CD passes through the circle centre O.

Note: The perpendicular bisector of the chord AB is also the bisector of the arc AB.

2 **To find the centre of a circle**

Draw a circle of diameter 72 mm.
Take any 3 points A, B and C on the circle.
Bisect the two arcs AB and BC.
The intersection of the two bisectors, O, is the centre of the circle.

Note: It follows that if any three points are taken, providing they are not in a straight line, a circle can be drawn through the three points. The circle centre can be found by using this method.

3 **To find the centre of an arc**

Draw an arc of radius 70 mm.
Take any 3 points A, B and C on the arc.
Bisect the arcs AB and BC.
The centre O, of the arc is at the point of intersection of the bisectors.

4 **To draw a chord of given length in a circle**

Circle radius = 32 mm, chord AB = 55 mm.
Set compasses to 55 mm.
Select point A on the circle as one end of the arc.
With centre A and radius 55 mm strike arc B on the circle.
Join AB, which is the required chord.

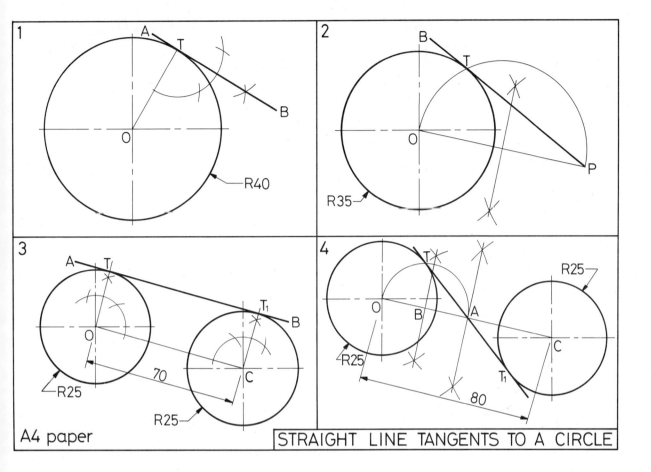

A4 paper

1 To construct a straight line tangent at a point on a circle

Circle, centre O, radius = 40 mm.
Take any point on the circumference T.
Join TO.
At T construct a right angle to the radius TO.
Then ATB is the required tangent.

Note: A straight line tangent forms a right angle with the radius at the point of tangency.

2 To construct a straight line tangent to a circle from a point outside the circle

Circle, centre O, radius = 35 mm.
Take any point P outside the circle.
Join OP.
Bisect OP.
Draw a semicircle on OP.
T, where the semicircle crosses the circle, is the point of tangency.
PTB is the required tangent.

Note: This construction is based upon the fact that the angle within a semicircle is a right angle.

3 To construct an external tangent to two equal circles

O and C are centres of two equal circles, each of radius 25 mm.
OC = 70 mm.
Join OC.
At O and at C construct OT and CT_1 at right angles to OC.
Where OT and CT_1 cross the circles are the two points of tangency.
Then ATT_1B is the required tangent.

Note: AB is parallel to the line OC joining the two centres.

4 To construct an internal tangent to two equal circles

O and C are centres of circles of radius = 25 mm.
OC = 80 mm.
Join OC.
Bisect OC at A.
Bisect OA at B.
With B as centre draw a semicircle on OA.
T is the point where the semicircle crosses circle O.
Join TA and produce to T_1.
Then TAT_1 is the required tangent.

35

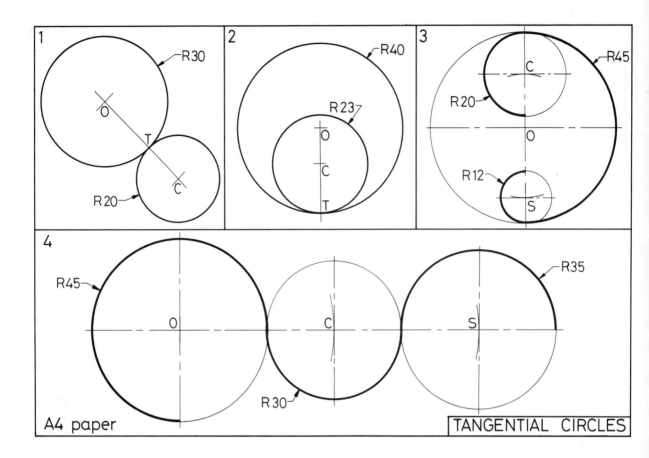

1 To construct a circle touching a given circle externally

Circle O, radius = 30 mm; circle C, radius = 20 mm.
Draw circle O.
Draw any line OT passing through centre O.
Set compasses to the sum of the two radii – 30 + 20
= 50 mm.
With centre O strike arc of 50 mm radius along line OT to give C.
Then C is the centre of the tangential circle.

Note: Because the line joining the centres of the two circles passes through their point of tangency it follows that an addition of the two radii is needed. This can be summarised as $R + r$ where R = radius of first circle and r = radius of tangential circle.

2 To construct a circle touching a given circle internally

Circle, centre O, radius = 40 mm; circle, centre C, radius = 23 mm.
Draw circle O.
Draw any line OT passing through centre O.
Set compasses to the difference between the two radii
= 40 – 23 = 17 mm.
With centre O strike arc of 17 mm along line OT to give C.
Then C is the centre of the required tangential circle.

Note: This can be summarised as $R - r$.

3 To construct a curve consisting of circular arcs

C, O and S are in a straight line.
Draw circle O.
Draw diameter through O.
With compasses set to 45 – 20 = 25 mm strike arc C on diameter.
With compasses set to 45 – 12 = 33 mm strike arc S on diameter.
The arcs of the curve can now be drawn on centres C, O and S.

4 Second example of a curve consisting of circular arcs

O, C and S are in a straight line.
Draw circle centre O.
Draw line OCS.
With centre O and radius 45 + 30 = 75 mm strike arc to obtain C.
With centre C and radius 30 + 35 = 65 mm strike arc to obtain S.
The arcs of the curve can now be drawn at centres O, C and S.

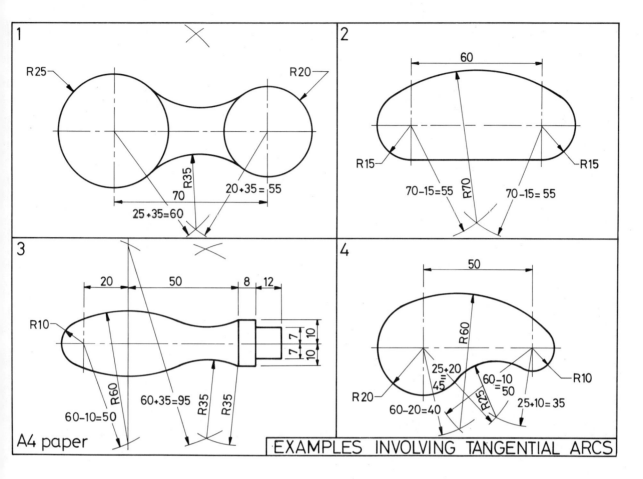

1 View of casting

Draw the two circles of radius 25 mm and 20 mm with their centres 70 mm apart.

Set compasses to 25 + 35 mm = 60 mm and draw arcs above and below the two circles.

Set compasses to 20 + 35 = 55 mm and draw arcs intersecting the 60 mm arcs.

Set compasses to 35 mm and draw the arcs completing the outline of the view of the casting.

2 Cover plate

Draw two circles of radius 15 mm with centres 60 mm apart.

Set compasses to 70 − 15 = 55 mm and from the centres of the R15 circles draw intersecting arcs which give the centre of the R70 arc to complete the outline.

3 Handle

Draw the outline of the file handle, working to the compass settings for the various arcs as shown on the drawing.

4 Spacer

Draw the outline of the spacer, working to the compass settings for the various arcs as shown in the drawing.

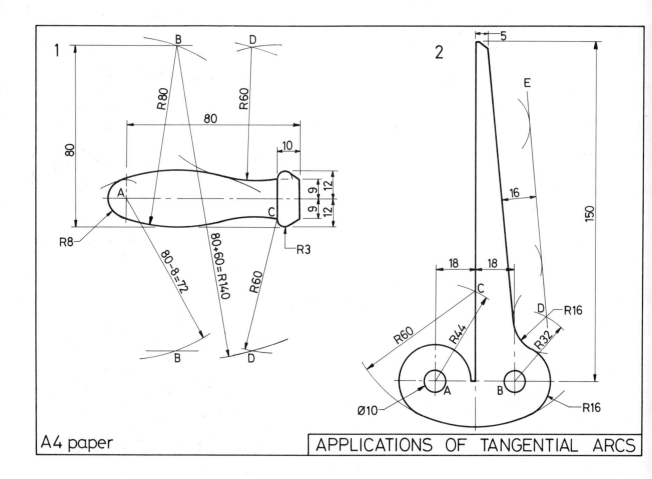

A4 paper

APPLICATIONS OF TANGENTIAL ARCS

1 To draw outline of file handle

Draw the centre line through the handle.

Draw lines 9 and 12 mm each side of and parallel to the centre line.

Draw lines 80 mm parallel to the 12 mm lines.

Draw verticals across the centre line at 10 mm and 80 mm from the right-hand end.

With compasses set to radii as shown, draw 8 mm and 72 mm arcs from point A.

With centres B draw 80 mm and 140 mm arcs as shown.

With centres C draw 60 mm arcs as shown.

With centres D draw 60 mm arcs as shown.

Draw the 3 mm radii at the right-hand end and complete the drawing.

2 To draw outline of centre finder

Draw the centre line along the centre finder.

Draw a second centre line at right angles to the main centre line and 150 mm from the upper end.

With centres A and B draw circles of radii 5 mm and 16 mm.

With the same centres draw an arc of radius 44 mm to obtain point C on main centre line.

With centre C draw an arc of radius 60 mm.

Draw line from 5 mm width to B.

Draw DE parallel to and 16 mm from this line.

With centre B and radius 16 + 16 = 32 mm draw an arc to give D.

With centre D and radius 16 mm draw a radius curve.

Complete the drawing as above.

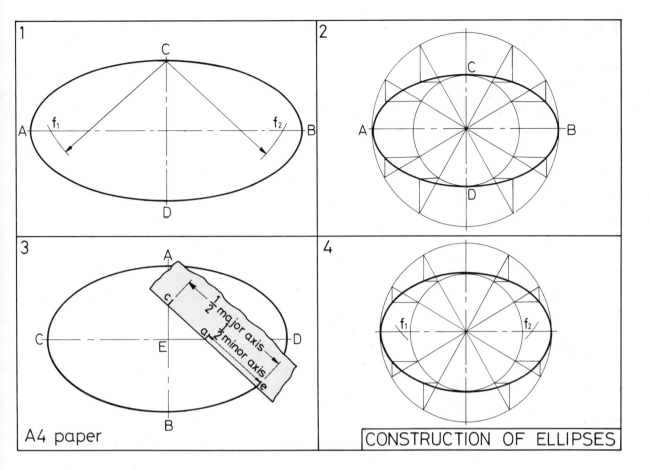

A4 paper

CONSTRUCTION OF ELLIPSES

1 The ellipse
The curve is an **ellipse**.
AB is the **major axis** of the ellipse.
CD is the **minor axis** of the ellipse.
f_1 and f_2 are the two **focal points** (or **foci**) of the ellipse.
$Cf_1 = Cf_2 = \frac{1}{2}$ major axis.
$Cf_1 + Cf_2 =$ major axis.

To find the two focal points:
Set compasses to half the major axis and with centre C strike arcs across the major axis at f_1 and f_2.

2 Auxiliary circles method of constructing an ellipse
Major axis AB = 110 mm, minor axis CD = 55 mm.
Draw two concentric circles, one of the major axis diameter, one of the minor axis diameter.
Draw a number of diameters across both circles. Where each diameter touches the larger circle draw verticals towards the major axis.
Where each diameter touches the smaller circle draw horizontals outwards to meet these verticals.
The right-angle corners formed by the horizontals meeting the verticals are points on the curve of the ellipse.
Draw a fair curve through these points to complete the ellipse.

3 Trammel method of drawing an ellipse
Major axis CD = 110 mm, minor axis AB = 70 mm.
Draw AB and CD.
Cut a strip of paper with one edge straight to use as a trammel.
On the straight edge of the trammel mark half the major axis and within this, half the minor axis. This gives ce and ae on the trammel.
Move the trammel to various positions so that the mark c is always on the minor axis and the mark a is always on the major axis.
Mark the position of e on your paper at the various positions of the trammel.
When sufficient marks have been made on your paper, draw a fair freehand curve through the points to complete the ellipse.

4 Ellipse on axes 80 mm and 50 mm drawn using the auxiliary circles method of construction
Focal points f_1 and f_2 have also been constructed.

Exercises

Note

The auxiliary circles method of constructing an ellipse is a good geometrical method. The trammel method of drawing an ellipse is a good workshop method.

The solutions to the exercises on this page can all be drawn on both sides of an A3 size sheet of drawing paper.

1 An elliptical table-top is to be cut from a rectangular piece of wood 1.3 m by 0.8 m. To a scale of 1 in 10 show how you would produce the ellipse. (*North West*)

2 A drawing of a layout for a greetings card is shown. Copy the drawing to a scale of 1:1 (*full size*) showing *all* constructions necessary to obtain the ellipse and the pentagon. (*West Midlands*)

3 Construct the semielliptical arch of this bridge. The span is AB and the maximum height CD. Set squares may be used. (*South East*)

4 AB is the elevation of a circular piece of tinplate 90 mm in diameter.
Use a suitable geometrical construction to draw the plan view of AB. All construction lines must be shown. (*ALSEB*)

5 The drawing shows an elliptical cover plate with 10 fixing holes drilled at the focal points of the ellipse. Construct an accurate scale 1:1 drawing of the cover plate.

6 The drawing shows the panel for a transistor radio. Make a scale 1:2 drawing of the panel showing all the construction necessary to obtain the elliptical curve and the spacing of the four control knob holes.

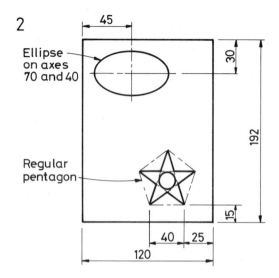

2

Ellipse on axes 70 and 40

Regular pentagon

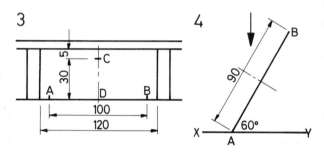

3

4

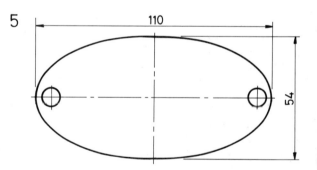

5

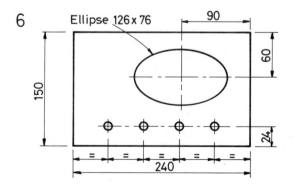

6 Ellipse 126 x 76

40

7 $X+$ $+Y$

XY = 45 mm
YZ = 55 mm
ZX = 50 mm

$+Z$

7 Use a geometrical construction to find the centre of a circle whose circumference passes through the points XYZ.

8 An incomplete geometrical construction is given.
(a) Complete it.
(b) State what the construction does.
(East Anglia, South)

9 (a) What is the name given to the line AB shown in the figure?
(b) Draw the circle shown of 80 mm diameter and position point P; at this point construct a tangent.

10 The drawing shows part of a large broken concrete water pipe the diameter of which could not be measured. A straightedge was laid parallel to the ground and the measurements were taken as shown.
Make a construction, using a scale of 100 mm = 1 m, which would enable you to find the internal diameter of the pipe. Draw the cross section of the pipe and enter the full size measurement of the internal diameter. *(Welsh)*

11 Add a 40 mm diameter circle to touch the two given circles, showing constructions quite clearly.

12 Name the parts of the drawing. *(ALSEB)*

8

● Point

9

A

B

Ø80

15

P

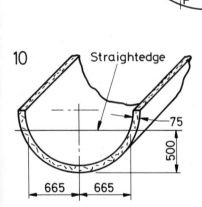

10 Straightedge

75

500

665 665

11

Ø50

+

Ø20

+

12 Name this line

Name this figure

90°

Name this line

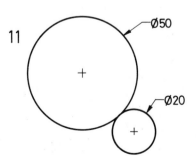

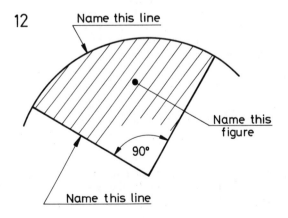

Exercises

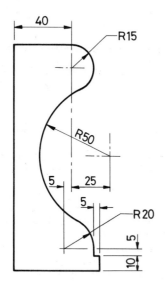

13

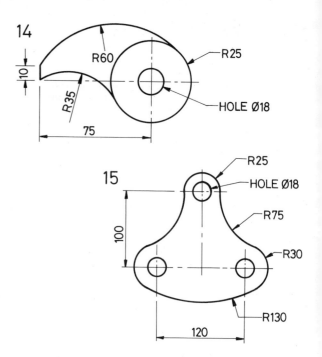

14

15

16

17

18

13 The outline of a reconstructed stone plinth is shown.
Using a geometrical construction make an accurate copy of this section, all centres of arcs to be clearly shown.
(*North West*)

14 Complete a scale 1:1 view of the pawl shown. Indicate clearly the construction by which the centres of the required arcs are located. Show all points of tangency. (*ALSEB*)

15 The dimensioned drawing shows a handle bracket from a paint can.
Draw the handle bracket, *full size.*
Clearly show the constructions for finding the centres for the blending arcs. (*South Western*)

16 The outline and pictorial representation of a heavy duty foot pedal are shown. Draw, full size to the dimensions given, the outline of the pedal showing clearly the geometrical construction for the quarter ellipse and the joining of each curve.
(*East Anglian, North*)

17 One blade of a cooling fan is shown. Redraw the given view showing all construction lines and points of tangency. (*East Anglian, North*)

18 Draw, *full size*, the outline of the car tail light. Clearly show your constructions for the ½ ellipse and the ½ regular octagon. (*East Midland*)

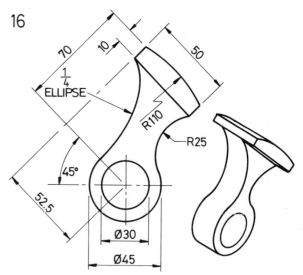

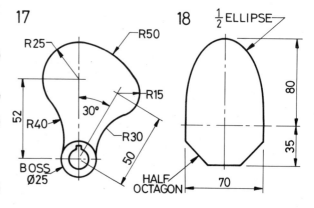

Exercises (Revision)

1 A clear plastic drawing template is shown.
(a) Draw, full size, the given outline.
(b) Find, by geometrical construction, the centre of each of the holes on two of its sides.
(c) Construct, using compasses, each of the three angles 30°, 45° and 60°. You are not required to draw the projection symbols, the small circles representing the holes, or the arrow head. (*East Anglian, South*)

2 The roof structure for a small factory is triangular in shape as shown. Within the triangle are two supports which form part of an irregular polygon ABCDE.
The sides of this polygon are in the following ratio:
AB : BC : CD : DE : EA
2 : 3 : 3 : 3 : 3
and the perimeter of the irregular polygon is 12 metres. The angles EAS and CBN are each 60°. Find by drawing to a scale of 20 mm representing 1 metre, the actual span of the roof. (*East Anglian, South*)

3 Make a scale 1:1 drawing of the checking gauge shown. The 60 degree and 105 degree angles must show evidence of compasses construction.
No marks will be awarded if a protractor is used. (*ALSEB*)

4 A sign designer's letter T is too small. Enlarge the given letter so that side AB is enlarged to AC, using a constructional method. (*East Anglian, South*)

5 A sign board in the shape of a true ellipse is to be bolted onto a bracket above a shop entrance. The major and minor axis of the ellipse are 1200 mm × 800 mm respectively.
Two fixing holes for bolts are to have their centres located on the focal points of the ellipse.
Construct the ellipse to a scale of 1:10 (do not use the trammel method) and mark clearly the centres for the bolt holes. (*East Anglian, North*)

6 (a) Draw two circles, each of diameter 45 mm, with their centres 90 mm apart. Construct both internal tangents common to the two circles.
(b) Draw a circle of radius 25 mm. Select a point 35 mm outside the circumference of the circle and from this point construct a tangent to the circle.
(c) Draw three circles of radius 15 mm, 20 mm and 30 mm each touching the other.

1

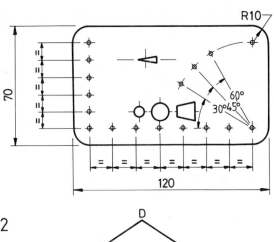

2

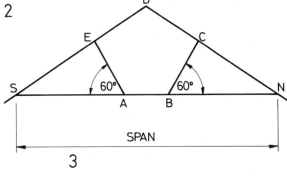

3

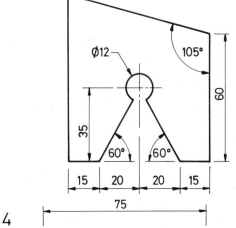

4

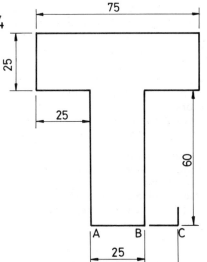

43

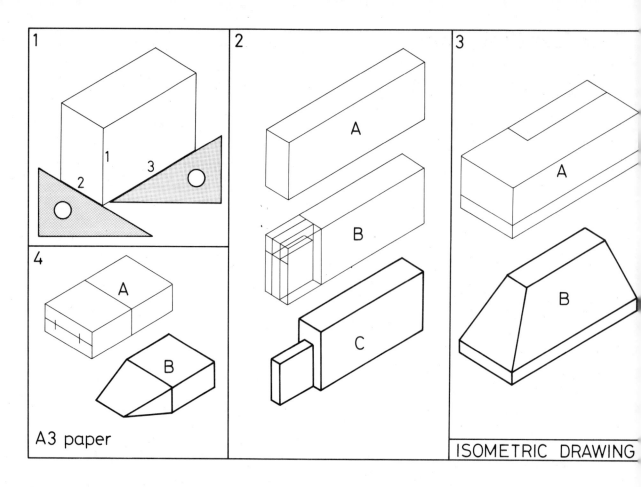

A3 paper

ISOMETRIC DRAWING

1 Isometric drawing of a block

The block is 70 mm long by 50 mm high by 30 mm deep.
Commence by drawing lines 1, 2 and 3 with the aid of a
30°, 60° set square. Line 1 is vertical, lines 2 and 3 are 30°
to the horizontal.
Measure the height – 50 mm along line 1, the depth –
30 mm along line 2, and the length – 70 mm along line 3.
From the points so obtained complete the drawing using
a set square to obtain the angles.

Note: Isometric drawing is a convenient method of obtaining a
pictorial view of any object. It is particularly useful for making
pictorial views of furniture parts and engineering components.

When making an isometric drawing two rules should be
observed:
1. If at all possible, commence by drawing a box such as
the above, showing maximum length, height and depth
of the object being drawn.
2. *All* measurements *must* be made either along vertical
lines or along the lines at 30° to the horizontal.

2 Isometric drawing of a tenon

A: isometric box containing whole of piece of wood –
100 mm by 35 mm by 15 mm.
B: tenon constructed within the end of the isometric box.
C: isometric drawing lined in and construction lines not
needed erased.

3 Isometric drawing of block with bevels

A: block 95 mm by 40 mm by 30 mm constructed as an
isometric box.
Part remaining when bevels cut marked out with
measurements taken along isometric axes.
Bevel at end 35 mm by 23 mm.
Bevel at side 25 mm by 23 mm.
B: isometric drawing lined in. Construction lines should
now be erased.

4 Isometric drawing of a wedge

A: block 60 mm by 35 mm by 15 mm constructed as an
isometric box.
Width of wedge 20 mm at end. Wedge 30 mm long.
Construction for wedge drawn in construction lines.
B: isometric drawing lined in. Construction lines should
now be erased.

44

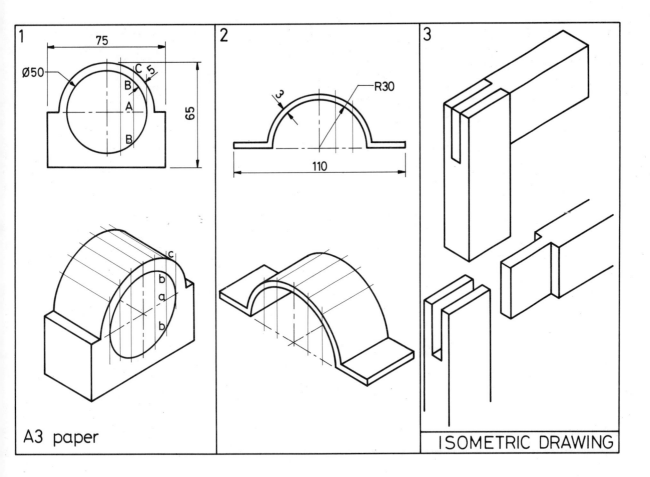

A3 paper

ISOMETRIC DRAWING

1 Isometric drawing of a clock case
Block 75 mm long by 65 mm high by 35 mm deep.
Hole = 50 mm diameter. Thickness around hole = 5 mm.
Construct a front view of the clock case and divide by
vertical ordinates such as ABC as shown.
Construct the isometric box for the clock case.
Copy the ordinates by measuring from the face view on
to the isometric box, measuring along isometric axes.
Transfer the lengths of the ordinates from the front view
to the isometric box with compasses. Two lengths AB
and AC are shown so transferred to ab and ac.
Construction lines can now be rubbed out.

2 Isometric drawing of a half brass
Made from material 3 mm thick.
Length = 110 mm, width = 35 mm.
Made to take a diameter 60 mm spindle.
Construct an isometric box only for the circular part of
the half brass.
Then proceed as for the clock case in Space 1.
Construction lines can be rubbed out after the drawing
has been lined in.

3 Exploded isometric drawing
Two pieces 90 mm by 30 mm by 18 mm joined by a bridle
joint, the tenon of which is 6 mm thick.
The upper isometric drawing shows the assembled joint.
The lower drawing shows the exploded drawing.
The piece containing the tenon is shown as if pulled out
of its open mortise in the direction of one of the isometric
axes.

Notes
1. Exploded isometric drawings are a form of drawing frequently
used to show such details as woodwork jointing and mechanical
and engineering assemblies.
2. When drawing answers to questions in examinations, do **not**
erase construction lines.

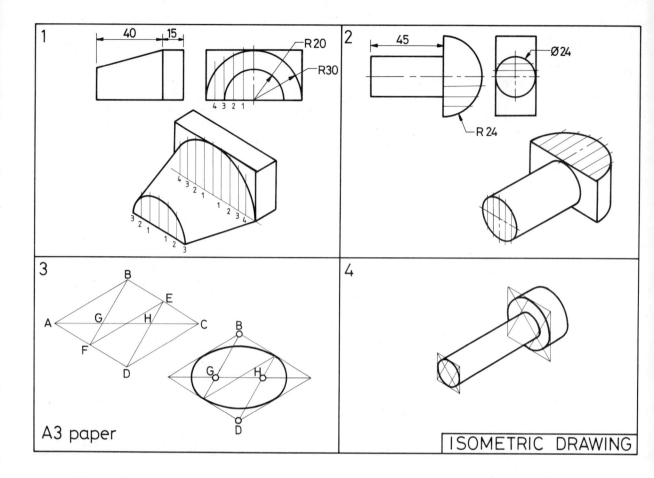

In panel 3: A3 paper

1 Isometric drawing involving curves in one view

The two semicircles in the upper drawings show the true shape of each end of the half cone. Ordinates 1 to 4 have been drawn vertically on them.

Construct the rectangular prism using the 30° angle of a set square for the sloping lines.

The three centre lines can next be drawn and then the base lines of the semicircular ends.

Copy the ordinates on to the isometric drawing, taking measurements along the bases from the upper drawing. Using compasses measure and mark the lengths of the ordinates on to the isometric drawing from the top drawing.

Draw freehand curves through the marks so obtained. Complete the drawing as shown.

Erase any unwanted construction.

2 Isometric drawing involving curves in both views

The method employed to make the isometric drawing is the same as that used in the previous example. Ordinates from the orthographic views are copied on to the isometric drawing to obtain points on the isometric curves.

3 Compasses method of constructing circles in an isometric drawing

To construct an isometric drawing of a diameter 55 mm circle.

Construct the parallelogram ABCD of 55 mm side lengths with 30° set square.

Draw diagonal AC.

From B and D draw lines with a 60° set square to meet BC and AD in E and F. E and F are the midpoints of the sides BC and AD.

With centres G and H draw arcs touching each of the four sides of the parallelogram.

With centres B and D draw longer arcs touching the sides of the parallelogram and meeting the smaller arcs.

Note: This is an approximate method and is only suitable for making isometric drawings of circles or arcs of radii less than about 15 mm.

4 Using the arcs method of constructing an isometric drawing

A cylinder of length 60 mm and diameter 16 mm is joined centrally to a cylinder 12 mm long and of diameter 30 mm. The constructions of the curves have been left on the isometric drawing to show how the method has been applied.

Exercises

1 Two views are given of a clock case. Make a scale 1:1 isometric drawing of the clock case showing all hidden detail.

2 Make a scale 1:1 isometric drawing of the tractor towing hitch shown by two views.

3 A first angle orthographic projection of a block is shown.
Draw, full size, an isometric drawing of the block.
Arrange your drawing so that the curved end is to the left.
(East Anglian, South)

4 Make a scale 1:1 isometric drawing of the handle.

5 Construct a scale 1:1 isometric drawing of the vice jaw casting.

3

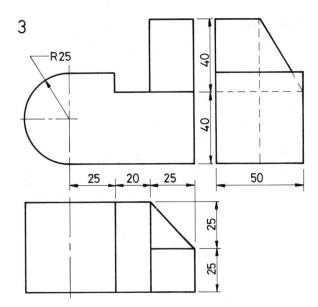

4

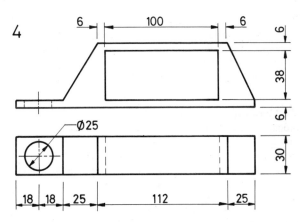

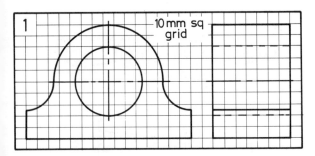

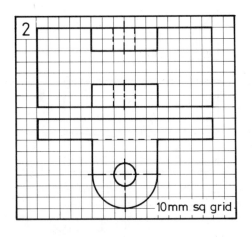

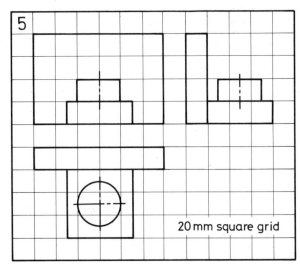

47

Exercises

6

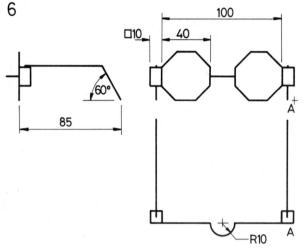

7

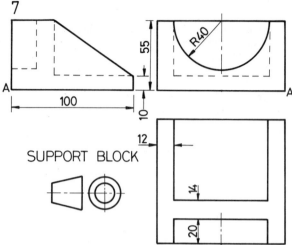

SUPPORT BLOCK

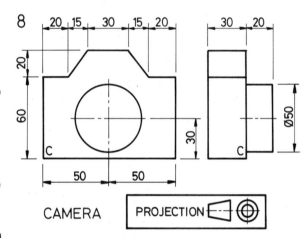

6 Construct, *full size*, an isometric drawing of the wire framed spectacles, with regular octagonal lenses.
The lenses to be vertical.
Do not show hidden detail.
Point A the lowest point of view. *(Southern)*

7 Make a full size isometric drawing of the support block. Make your drawing so that corner A is the lowest point.
Do not show hidden detail or dimension your drawing. *(East Anglian, South)*

8 Draw, *full size*, in isometric projection the camera, with corner C at the front of your drawing. *(East Midland)*

9 The drawings below show two views of a toy tank. Draw, *full size*, in isometric projection a view of this tank with corner B in the foreground. *(South Western)*

8

CAMERA

9

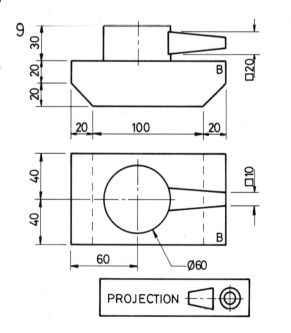

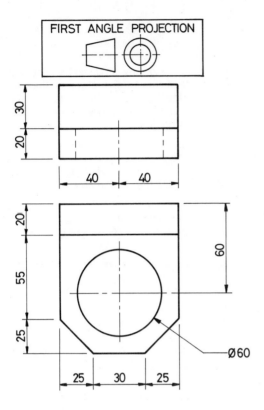

10

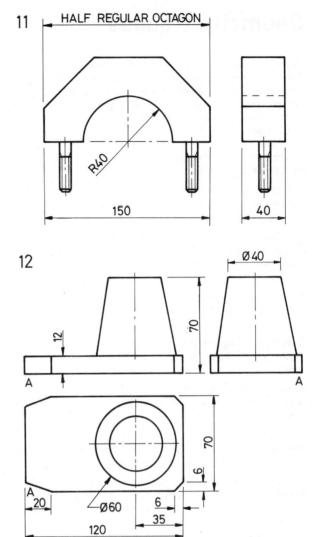

11 HALF REGULAR OCTAGON

12

13

10 The drawings show two views of a bathroom glass holder.
Draw, *full size*, an isometric drawing of the holder.
(*East Midland*)

11 A front view and end view of a door handle are given. Make a scale 1:1 (full size) isometric drawing of the handle. The screws should not be included in your drawing. Hidden detail is not required.   (*West Midland*)

12 The drawing shows three views of a casting for a stand for supporting a post in a vertical position.
Make a *full size* isometric drawing of the stand.
Corner A should be the lowest point on your drawing.
Construction must be shown of the method used to obtain the circular parts.

13 The drawing shows a front view and plan of a rubber stamp. Make a *full size* isometric drawing of the rubber stamp, with corner A as the lowest point on your drawing. No hidden detail is required.

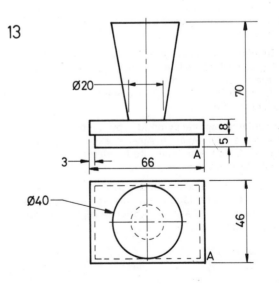

Geometrical solids

Twenty solids are shown on page 51 opposite. Projections and drawings of these solids will be found throughout the remainder of this book and in Book 2. All the solids shown here are 'right', in that a central axis taken vertically through each will be perpendicular to the face on which the solid is standing.

1. Cube: all edges of equal length and at right angles to each other. Each of the six faces is a square.

2. Rectangular prism: also named a **cuboid** – all edges at right angles to each other. Top and bottom faces rectangular. May be of any length vertically.

3. Triangular prism: top and bottom faces are triangular. May be of any vertical height. The prism may be named after the shape of its triangular faces – equilateral triangular prism, right-angled triangular prism and so on.

4. Regular pentagonal prism: top and bottom faces are regular pentagons of the same size. May be of any vertical height.

5. Regular hexagonal prism: top and bottom faces are regular hexagons of the same size. May be of any vertical height.

6. Regular octagonal prism: top and bottom faces are regular octagons of the same size. May be of any vertical height.

7. Cylinder: cuts taken at right angles to the central axis will produce circles all of the same diameter. Top and bottom faces are circular. May be of any vertical height.

8. Triangular pyramid: another name for this solid is a **Tetrahedron**. A **regular tetrahedron** is a triangular pyramid in which each of the four faces is an equilateral triangle. In any pyramid all the sloping triangular faces join at a point – the apex of the pyramid.

9. Square pyramid: the base is a square, each of the four sloping faces is an isosceles triangle of equal size. Any cut taken through the solid parallel to the base will produce a square smaller than the base.

10. Regular pentagonal pyramid: the base is a regular pentagon. Each of the five sloping sides is an isosceles triangle of equal size. Any cut taken through this solid parallel to the base will produce a regular pentagon smaller than the base.

11. Regular hexagonal pyramid: a pyramid the base of which is a regular hexagon. Any cut taken through this solid parallel to the base will produce a regular hexagon smaller than the base.

12. Regular octagonal pyramid: a pyramid the base of which is a regular octagon. Any cut taken through this solid parallel to the base will produce a regular octagon smaller than the base.

13. Cone: circular base. Any cut taken parallel to the base produces a circle of smaller diameter than the base. This is a solid of considerable importance in technical drawing because it is the basis of many three-dimensional shapes of objects in common use.

14. Sphere: any cut in any direction will produce a circle. Cuts passing through the centre of the sphere produce circles named as 'great' circles of the sphere. Great circles of a sphere are the same diameter as the sphere itself.

15. Truncated triangular prism: a triangular prism which has been cut at an angle other than 90° to the axis of the prism – in this case at 60° to the axis.

16. Truncated rectangular prism: a rectangular prism which has been cut at an angle other than 90° to the axis of the prism – in this case at 60° to the axis.

17. Truncated regular hexagonal prism: a regular hexagonal prism which has been cut at an angle other than 90° to the axis of the prism – in this case at 45° to the axis. The upper face of the solid is not a regular hexagon.

18. Truncated cone: a cone which has been cut at an angle other than 90° to the axis of the cone – in this case at 45° to the axis. The upper face of the cone is an ellipse.

19. Truncated square pyramid: a square pyramid which has been cut at an angle other than 90° to the axis of the pyramid – in this case at 45° to the axis. The upper face of the pyramid in this case is a trapezium.

20. Truncated regular octagonal pyramid: a regular octagonal pyramid which has been cut at an angle other than 90° to the axis of the pyramid – in this case at 30°. The upper face of the pyramid is not a regular octagon.

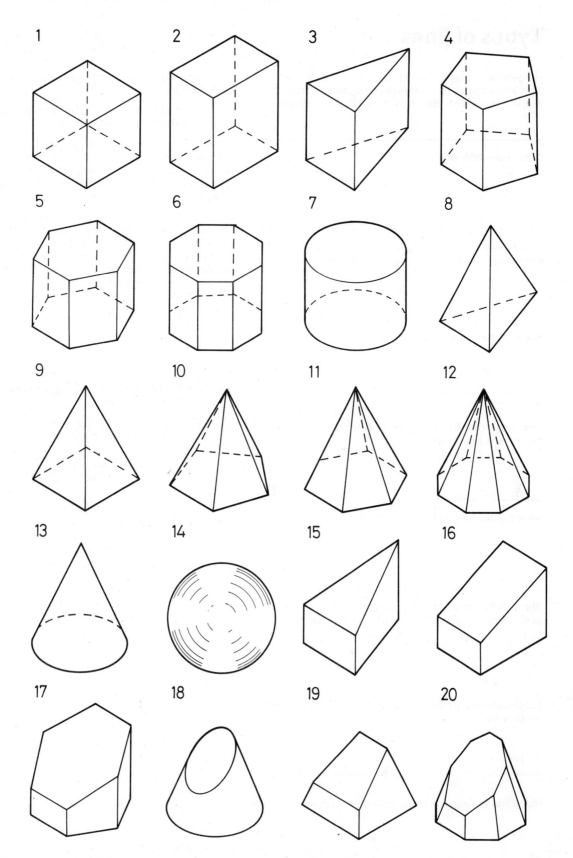

Types of lines

For general engineering purposes, the following types of lines should be used. These are as recommended in the British Standard BS 308 *Engineering Drawing Practice.*

Continuous (thick). Visible outlines.

Continuous (thin). Dimension lines; projection or extension lines; hatching or sectioning; leader lines for notes.

Short dashes (thin). Hidden detail.

Long chain (thin). Centre lines; path lines for indicating movement, pitch circles.

Long chain. Cutting or section planes.

Short chain (thin). Developed or false views; adjacent parts; features located in front of a cutting plane.

Continuous wavy (thin). Irregular boundary lines; short break lines.

Ruled line and zigzags (thin). Long break lines.

Lines should be sharp and dense to obtain good reproduction.

Lines specified as thick should be from two to three times the thickness of lines specified as thin.

Centre lines should project for a short distance beyond the outline to which they refer, but where necessary to permit dimensioning, they may be extended as projection lines. Centre lines should not intersect in the spaces between dashes.

Lines depicting hidden details should always begin and end with a dash in contact with the visible or hidden detail line at which they start or end, except when such a dash would form a continuation of a visible detail line. Dashes should join at corners, and arcs should start with dashes at the tangent points.

Blend lines and indefinite intersections may be thick or thin as advisable for clarity.

Types of letters and figures

ABCDEFGHIJKLMNOPQR
STUVWXYZ
1234567890

ABCDEFGHIJKLMNOPQRSTUVWXYZ
abcdefghijklmnopqrstuvwxyz
1234567890

ABCDEFGHIJKLMNOPQRSTUVWXYZ
abcdefghijklmnopqrstuvwxyz
1234567890

Information check-list

The following information should be included on the drawing sheet.

Title block

A title block suitable for use in schools is shown. Variations of this type of title block can be used, but the following minimum information should always be given:
1. Description or title of drawing.
2. Scale of drawing.
3. Date.
4. Name of person making the drawing.

The title block should preferably be placed in the bottom right-hand corner of the drawing sheet.

A name and form number has also been given. It is suggested that printing of 5 to 6 mm high be used in title blocks. A uniform height of lettering can be achieved by using guide lines for the lettering as suggested in the given title block.

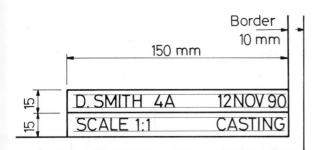

A title block suitable for a drawing on an A4 size sheet

Angle of projection

The angle of the projection – either First Angle projection or Third Angle projection. This should preferably be shown in symbol form.

Unit of measurement

The unit of measurement used. In this book all dimensions on machine drawings are in millimetres, and this is shown on the drawings.

Both the angle of projection and the unit of measurement should preferably be shown near the upper edge of the drawing sheet.

Border line

A border line or margin should be drawn inside every drawing sheet. This allows any damage to sheet edges to fall outside the drawing area.

Dimensions

Projection lines are thin full lines projected from points, lines or surfaces to enable the dimensions to be placed outside the outline wherever possible. Where projection lines are extensions of lines of the outline, they should preferably start just clear of the outline and should extend a little beyond the dimension line.

Dimension lines should be thin full lines and, wherever practicable, should be placed outside the outline of the object. Arrowheads should be easily readable and normally not less than 3 mm long. It is important that the point should touch the projection or other limiting line.

A centre line, or a line which is an extension of a centre line or part of an outline, should never be used as a dimension line.

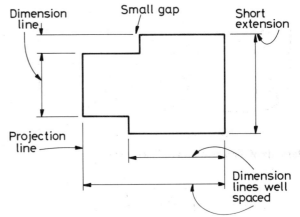

Drawing lines for dimensioning

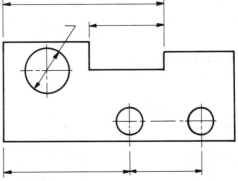

Positions of dimension lines and centre lines

Dimensions on drawings

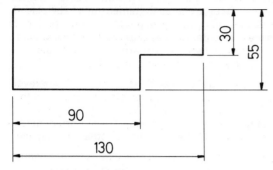

An example of dimensioning

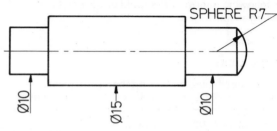

Methods of dimensioning rods and spherical curves

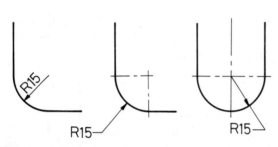

Methods of dimensioning radius curves

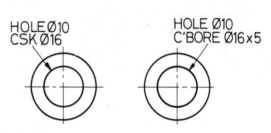

Methods of dimensioning countersunk and counterbored holes

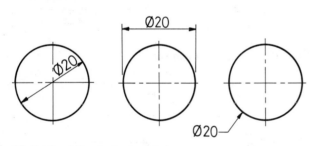

Methods of dimensioning circles

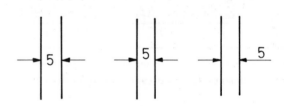

Methods of dimensioning small spaces or lengths

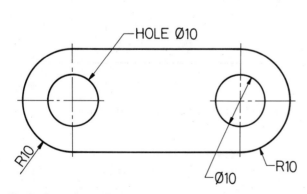

Methods of dimensioning holes and circular parts

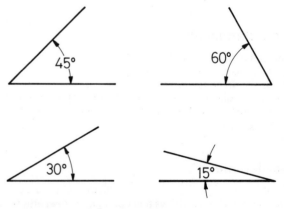

Methods of dimensioning angles

Planes used in orthographic projection

The basis of orthographic projection is that the object to be drawn is placed in one of the angles formed by a horizontal plane crossed as shown in drawing 1 by a vertical plane.

Planes at right angles to each other are said to be **orthogonal** to each other – hence **orthogonal** or **orthographic projection**.

When the object to be drawn has been projected on to the two planes, they are closed upon one another by being rotated as shown by the broken line arrow in drawing 1.

First Angle orthographic projection to obtain front view and plan

The object to be drawn, in this case part of a lathe tool post, is placed on the horizontal plane – the H.P. – a little in front of the vertical plane – the V.P. – as shown in drawing 2.

The object is viewed from the front, and what is seen is projected on to the V.P. – this projection is called a **front view** or a **front elevation**.
The object is viewed from above and what is seen is projected on to the H.P. – this projection is called a **plan**.
The object is removed from between the two planes.
The H.P. is then rotated to lie flat in the same plane as the V.P. as shown in drawing 3.
This produces a drawing showing a plan immediately below the front view.

Symbol of projection

The symbol of projection for drawings in First Angle is as shown in drawing 4.

1

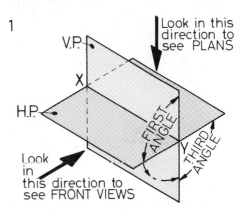

2

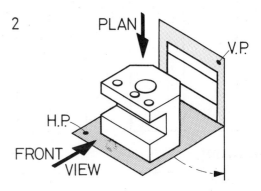

3

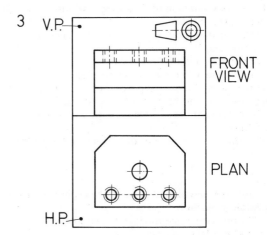

4

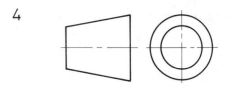

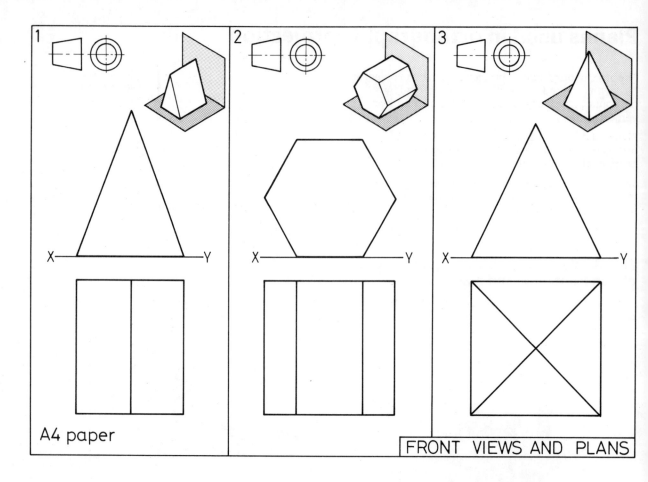

A4 paper

1 **Front view and plan of an isosceles triangular prism in First Angle projection**
Prism 60 mm long, sides of triangular face 50 mm, 70 mm and 70 mm long.
Rear of prism 10 mm in front of V.P.
Draw an XY line with the aid of a Tee square.
Construct the isosceles triangle of the front view.
Project the three vertical lines of the plan from the vertices of the triangle in the front view with the aid of a set square.
Draw the back and front lines of the plan with the aid of a Tee square.

2 **Front view and plan of a regular hexagonal prism in First Angle projection**
Prism 60 mm long, hexagon face edges 30 mm long.
Prism placed 10 mm in front of V.P.
Draw an XY line.
Construct the regular hexagon of the front view with the aid of a 30°, 60° set square.
Project the plan from the front view as shown.

3 **Front view and plan of a square pyramid in First Angle projection**
Base square edges each 60 mm long, vertical height of pyramid 60 mm.
Back edge of base 10 mm in front of the V.P.
Draw an XY line.
Construct the plan as shown – 10 mm below the XY line.
From the plan project the front view as shown with the aid of a set square.

Exercises

Worked example

1 Construct the front view and plan in fine construction lines as if the pyramid were resting flat on the H.P.
With centre C swing arcs on the front view through the apex A, through the far corner B, and through the centre point D.
Draw CB_1 at 30° to XY.
Draw D_1A_1 at right angles (with 60° set square) to CB_1.
Complete the correct front view as shown.
Project the plan from the front view.

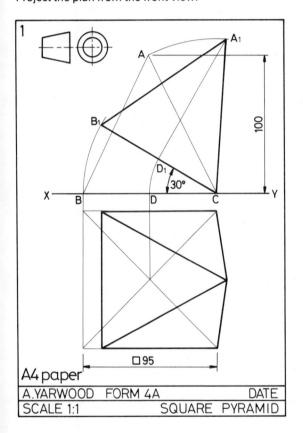

A4 paper

A.YARWOOD   FORM 4A   DATE
SCALE 1:1   SQUARE PYRAMID

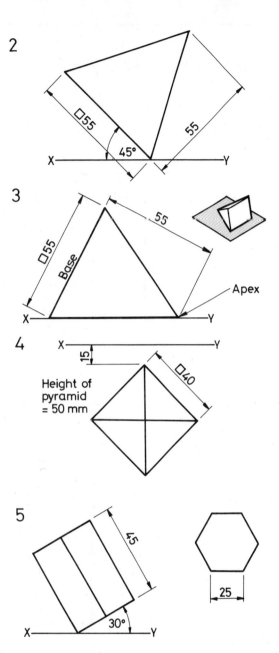

2 A front view of a square pyramid is given.
Its base is at 45° to the XY line. Draw the given front view and add a plan.
The rear edge of the base is 10 mm from the V.P.

3 A front view of a square pyramid is shown.
It is resting on one of its sloping sides.
The small pictorial view shows the position in which the pyramid is resting.
Draw the front view and add a plan.
The back edge of the base is 10 mm in front of the V.P.

4 The plan of a square pyramid is given.
Copy the plan and add a front view.

5 A regular hexagonal prism is placed so as to rest with one edge on the H.P. and the base tilted at 30° as shown.
The true shape of the base of the prism is given.
Draw scale 1:1 a front view and plan of the prism in the position shown.

DIMENSIONS IN MILLIMETRES

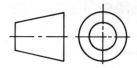

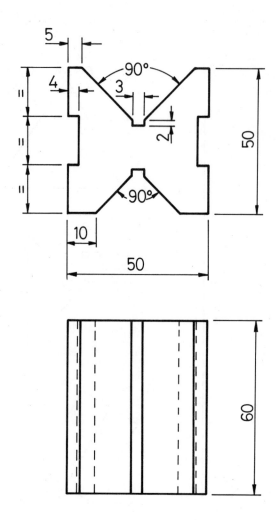

A. YARWOOD   FORM 4A   12 NOV 90

SCALE 1:1   V BLOCK

A First Angle projection of a V block

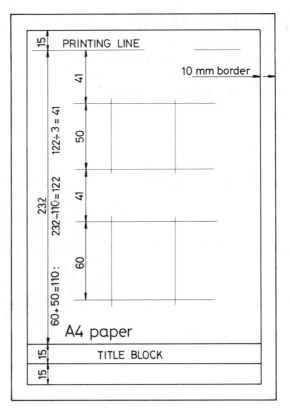

PRINTING LINE

10 mm border

A4 paper

TITLE BLOCK

The photograph shows a pair of V blocks in use on a surface plate ready for marking with the scriber in a scribing block. V blocks should be used in numbered pairs.

Layout of the drawing

The drawing of a V block on page 58 opposite has been drawn scale 1:1 on A4 paper. To achieve a presentable, well laid out drawing page, with a high standard of technique of draughtsmanship, should be the aim of every draughtsman. Such a drawing is pleasing to look at and more easily used than one which has been poorly laid out and badly drawn. Note the following:

1. Border line
On A4 paper, a border set in 10 mm from each edge enables the drawings to be placed in an area clear of possible damage to sheet edges.

2. Title block
All information concerning the drawing is gathered together in a title block. This information includes a descriptive name of the article drawn, the name of the draughtsman, the date on which the drawing was made and the scale to which it has been made. Other items of information can be included in the title block if thought fit. It is the usual practice to place the title block at the bottom of the drawing sheet inside the border.

3. Angle of projection
In this case – First Angle, as shown by the symbol. An important piece of information which should always be included on a drawing sheet.

4. Dimensioning units
Either the dimensioning units should be stated on the drawing sheet or they should be placed in abbreviated form against each dimension.

5. The position of views and plans
The position of views and plans should be planned before the drawing is started. The simplest way to achieve a good layout is shown in the drawing on this page.

Making the drawing

When the drawing sheet has been laid out as shown with the outlines of front view and plan drawn in very fine, light construction lines, proceed as follows:
1. Construct all the detail of the front view and plan using fine construction lines which can be easily erased should any mistakes occur. A 2H pencil should be used.
2. 'Line-in' the front view and plan with firm, quite black lines using a 2H pencil.
3. Resharpen the 2H pencil and draw in hidden detail lines, dimension lines and dimension projection lines. These lines should be thin, but black, about a half, or even a third, as wide as the outline lines already drawn.
4. Using an H or an HB pencil, carefully complete all dimension figures and place in the arrows at the ends of all dimension lines.
Arrows should be about 3 mm long.
Figures should stand about 5 or 6 mm high.
5. Draw very faint pencil lines with the aid of a Tee square at top and bottom of the sheet as guide lines for lettering, 4 mm high at the top, 5 or 6 mm high in the title block.
6. Draw in all the lettering at top and bottom with an H or HB pencil.
7. With a clean pencil eraser, erase any unwanted construction lines.

Exercise

Copy the drawing on page 58 using an A4 sheet of paper.

59

Gear striker fork

The photograph shows a gear striker fork. In the given drawing, a start has been made on a two-view First Angle orthographic drawing of the striker fork.

Exercise

Copy the given drawing scale 1:1 on a sheet of A4 size drawing paper.
Add a front view.
Fully dimension the drawing.

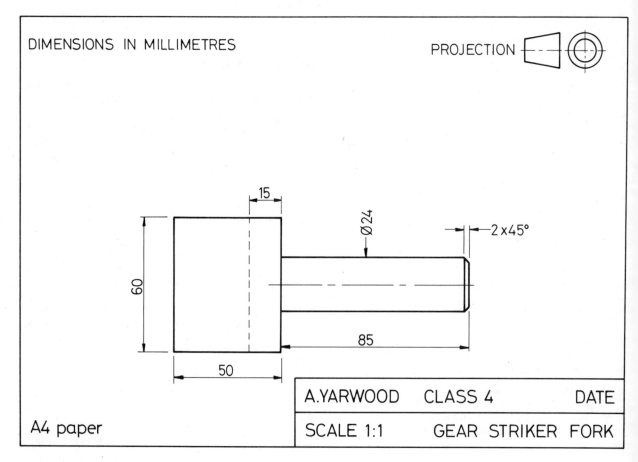

DIMENSIONS IN MILLIMETRES

PROJECTION

A.YARWOOD	CLASS 4	DATE
SCALE 1:1	GEAR STRIKER FORK	

A4 paper

Grinding wheel tool rest

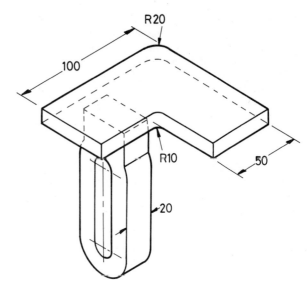

Exercise

A grinding wheel tool rest is shown in the photograph and in a dimensioned isometric drawing. A front view of the tool rest is given. Use A3 size paper. Draw a border 12 mm in from each edge of the paper. Draw a title block. Draw, scale 1:1, in First Angle projection:

    (a) The given front view,

    (b) a plan beneath the front view.

Add to your drawings all measurements you consider necessary to dimension the tool rest fully.

Print your name, the date, scale and the title TOOL REST in the title block.

Add the symbol for the angle of projection.

Add DIMENSIONS IN MILLIMETRES.

Notes

Centre lines must always be shown through the centres of all circular parts.

Line-in all circles and arcs before lining-in straight lines.

Hidden detail should be shown.

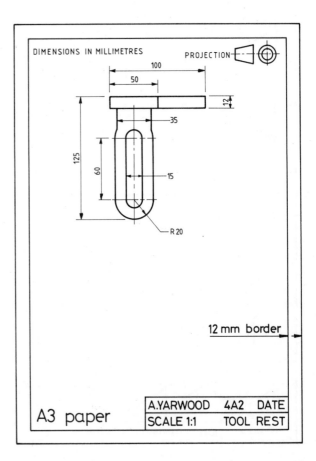

Exercises

The illustrations on this page have been drawn on 10 mm isometric grids. In order to determine the dimensions of the parts of each object shown in the drawings count the numbers of sides of the triangles making up the isometric grid. Multiply the figures so obtained by 10. Thus in drawing 1 the base of the bearing block is 10 triangle sides long = 10 × 10 = 100 mm by 3 triangle sides deep = 3 × 10 mm = 30 mm.

1 Draw a First Angle orthographic projection of the plain bearing to a scale of 1:1 showing a front view and a plan.

2 Draw, scale 1:1, in First Angle projection, the following two views of the shackle shown:
    (**a**) a front view as seen in the direction of the arrow F,
    (**b**) a plan.

3 An isometric drawing of a slide is shown. Draw, scale 1:1, in First Angle projection, a front view and plan of the slide. Look in the direction of the arrow F to obtain the required front view.

4 Draw, scale 1:1, in First Angle projection, a front view and plan of the stand shown in drawing 4.

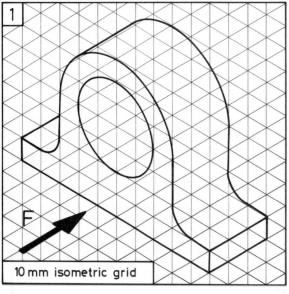

10 mm isometric grid

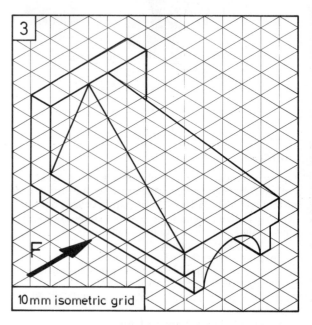

10 mm isometric grid

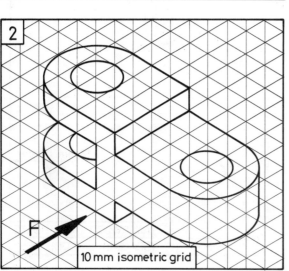

10 mm isometric grid

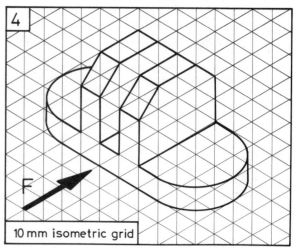

10 mm isometric grid

5

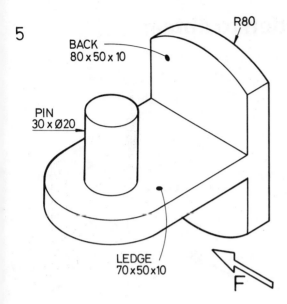

R80
BACK
80 x 50 x 10
PIN
30 x Ø20
LEDGE
70 x 50 x 10
F

6

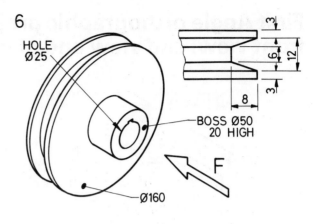

HOLE
Ø 25
BOSS Ø50
20 HIGH
Ø160
F

3
6
12
3
8

7

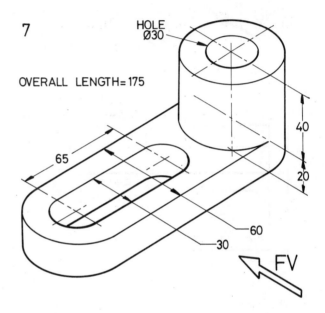

HOLE
Ø30
OVERALL LENGTH = 175
65
40
20
60
30
FV

5 An isometric drawing of a gate hinge pin is given.
Draw, scale 1:1, in First Angle projection, a front view as
seen in the direction of arrow F and a plan.

6 Draw, scale 1:1, a front view and a plan in First Angle
projection of the pulley shown. The front view should be
drawn as viewed from the arrow F.
The small drawing shows details of the groove for the
pulley belt.
Fully dimension and add a title block.

7 An isometric drawing of part of a lathe tool rest is
shown.
Draw, scale 1:1, in First Angle projection:
    (**a**) a front view as seen from FV,
    (**b**) a plan.
Use an A4 sheet of paper.
Fully dimension the drawing and add a suitable title
block.

8 A bracket is shown in front view. Its depth from front
to back is 140 mm. Copy the given view and add a plan.
Show all hidden detail, fully dimension and add a
suitable title block.

8

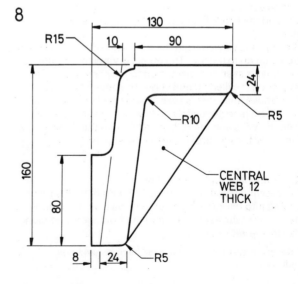

130
R15
10
90
24
R10
R5
160
80
CENTRAL
WEB 12
THICK
8
24
R5

First Angle orthographic projection to obtain front view, end view and plan

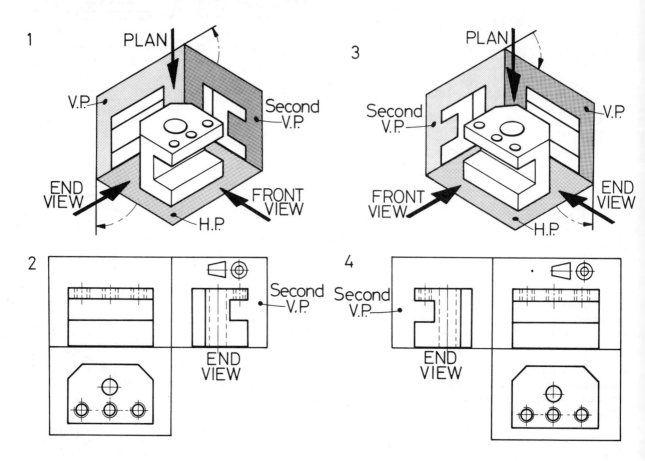

1 The object to be drawn, the lathe tool post shown on page 55, is placed on the H.P. a little in front of the V.P. A second vertical plane is placed at right angles to both the H.P. and the first V.P. and to the right-hand side of the object.

The object is viewed from the front and what is seen is projected on to the V.P. The object is viewed from the left and what is seen is projected on to the second V.P. This projection is called an **end view**. The object is viewed from above and what is seen is projected on to the H.P. The object is removed from between the three planes. Both the V.P.s and the H.P. are rotated in the directions as shown by the two broken line arrows to lie flat.

2 Front view, end view and plan
The drawing resulting from the H.P. and the V.P.s being rotated into the same plane shows the front view and end view in line with each other and the front view and plan also in line with each other.

Note: In this case the end view is on the right-hand side of the front view.

3 End view on left of front view
A second V.P. placed to the left-hand side of the object. Object removed and planes rotated in the direction of the broken line arrows.

4 Front view, end view and plan
The drawing shows the result of rotating the two V.P.s and H.P. into the same plane.

Note: In this case the end view is on the left-hand side of the front view.
Either, or both, end views can be included in the drawing, depending upon the shape of the object being drawn. The aim should be to select the views giving the best interpretation of the object.

Three-view First Angle orthographic projection

A photograph and a completed three-view First Angle orthographic projection of a V-block are given. A smaller drawing shows the layout for the three views. Compare this layout with that shown for a two-view drawing on page 59.

Exercise

Copy the given drawing on an A4 size drawing sheet.

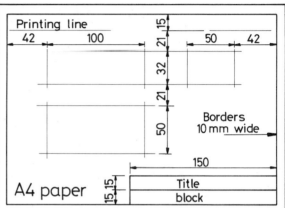

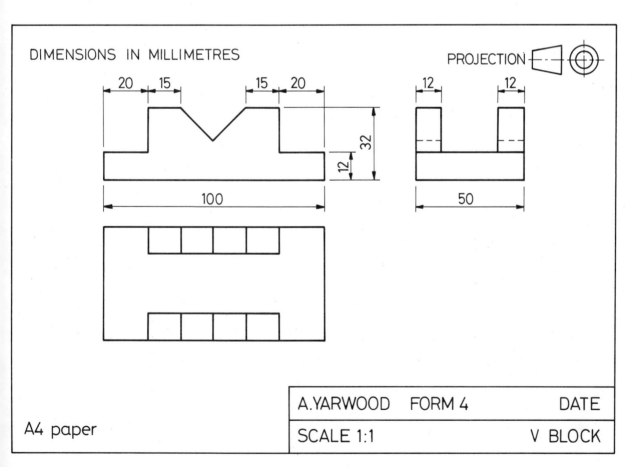

DIMENSIONS IN MILLIMETRES

PROJECTION

A.YARWOOD	FORM 4	DATE
SCALE 1:1		V BLOCK

A4 paper

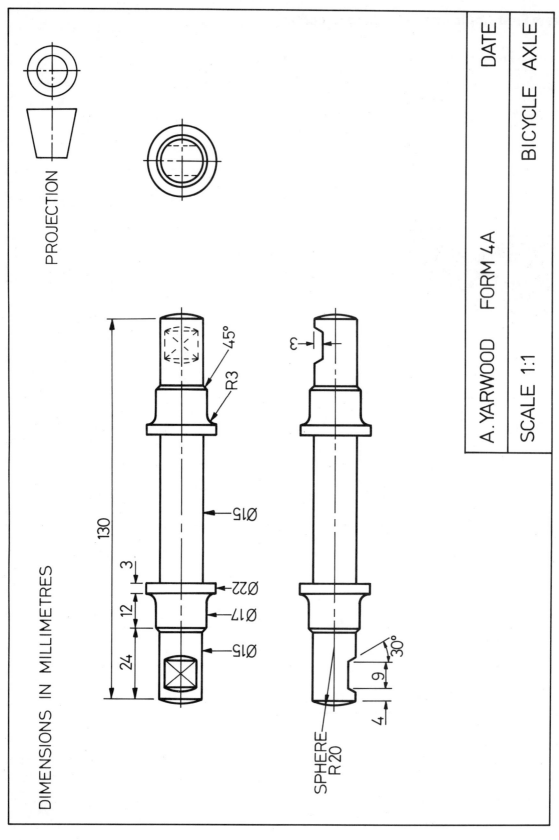

DIMENSIONS IN MILLIMETRES

PROJECTION

130

3

12

24

R3

45°

Ø15

Ø22

Ø17

Ø15

3

30°

9

4

SPHERE
R 20

| A. YARWOOD | FORM 4A | DATE |
| SCALE 1:1 | | BICYCLE AXLE |

Front view, end view and plan in First Angle projection of a cycle axle

Many engineering components are cylindrical in shape or are composed of circular parts. All cylindrical and circular detail should be drawn on centre lines.

The quickest and most accurate method of obtaining a sheet layout when drawing components comprising cylinders and circular parts is to base the layout around the centre lines. The three small drawings on this page show the step by step process of laying out the drawing of the cycle axle shown on page 66 opposite.

Drawing procedure

1. Use an A4 sheet of paper. Draw a border line 10 mm in from each edge and draw the title block borders as shown in drawing 1.
2. Lay out the centre lines as shown in drawing 1. The arithmetic for this can be worked on a piece of scrap paper.
3. Construct the two views and the plan, building up all three together – drawings 2 and 3.
4. Line-in all circles and arcs. Radius curves, if available, may be used for the quadrants on the front view and plan. Use an H or HB pencil lead in your compasses to obtain firm black lines.
5. Line-in all straight lines using a 2H pencil to obtain firm, black lines.
6. Draw all dimension lines, dimension projection lines and hidden detail lines using a sharp 2H pencil to obtain thin, black lines.
7. Print measurements and draw in arrowheads using an H or an HB pencil.
8. Print the lettering at the top and in the title block with a sharp H or HB pencil working between faint guide lines – 4 mm apart at top, 5 or 6 mm in the title block.
9. Erase any unwanted construction.

Note: In this particular drawing either the left-hand or the right-hand end views could have been selected, because they are identical to each other.
It is a common practice, when either end view gives sufficient information for drawing purposes, to select the one appearing on the right-hand side of the front view. This is the view seen when the object being drawn is viewed from the left.

Exercise

Copy the drawing on page 66 using an A4 piece of paper.

1

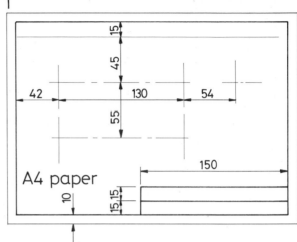

2

3

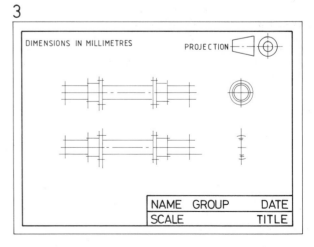

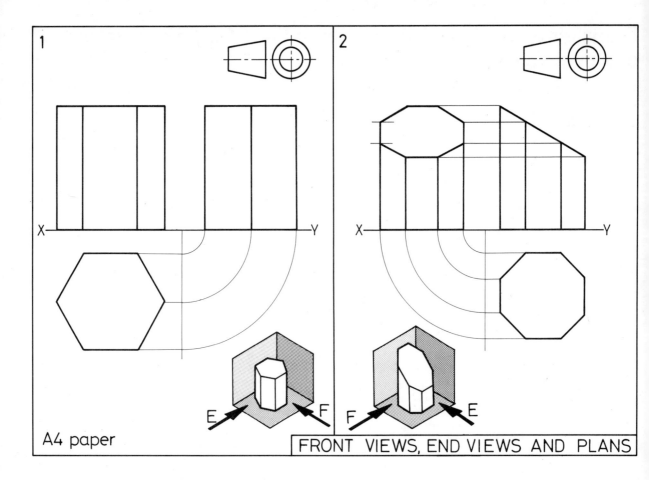

FRONT VIEWS, END VIEWS AND PLANS

A4 paper

1 Front view, end view and plan in First Angle projection of a regular hexagonal prism

Sides of hexagonal base each 25 mm long, height of prism 55 mm, back of prism 10 mm in front of V.P. Draw front view and plan.

Select any position along the XY line to the right of the plan and draw a vertical line as shown.

With the aid of a Tee square project lines and points from the plan on to this line.

With compasses on the intersection of this line with the XY line and with radii set to the projection points on it from the plan, draw quadrant arcs as shown.

The end view can now be drawn projected from the front view and from the ends of the quadrant arcs on the XY line.

2 Front view, end view and plan in First Angle projection of a truncated octagonal prism

Each side of octagonal base 16 mm long, maximum height 55 mm, truncated surface at 30° to horizontal. Proceed as in drawing 1, except that, in this case, the prism is best viewed from the right to obtain an end view giving the most information.

Because of this the end view is to the left of the front view.

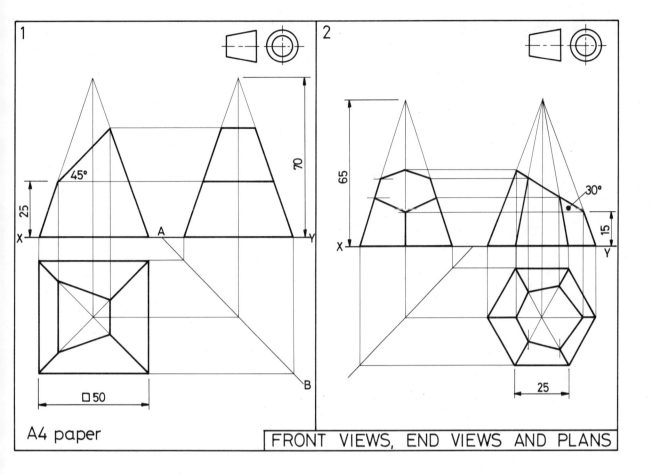

A4 paper

Front views, end views and plans of truncated solids
In the two worked examples shown on this page lines drawn at 45° to the XY line have been used to project details of the plans into the end views. Compare this method with that shown on page 68 opposite. Either method is suitable and the student should choose that which he or she prefers.

1 Front view, end view and plan of a truncated square pyramid
Draw a front view and a plan of the pyramid before truncation.
Draw the truncation line on the front view and project the truncated surface into the plan.
Project details from the plan on to the 45° line AB.
Complete the end view by projections upwards from line AB and horizontally from the front view.

2 Front view, end view and plan of a truncated hexagonal pyramid
In this example the end view is shown to the left of the front view because the truncated surface is best viewed from the right.
Proceed as for the truncated square pyramid drawing—draw the plan and front view prior to truncation.
Add the truncation line to the front view. Project the truncated surface into the plan. Draw a line at 45° to XY and project details from the plan on to this line.
Project from the 45° line and from the front view to complete the end view.

Clamping block

The photograph shows a clamping block such as would be used to assist in clamping work to the face plate of a lathe. An isometric drawing of the block is also shown.

Exercise

Copy the details given in the drawing on this page by preparing an A3 sheet for a three-view First Angle orthographic projection of the block. Copy the given plan and add a front view and an end view.
Do not copy the isometric drawing.
Dimension your drawing.
Add hidden detail.

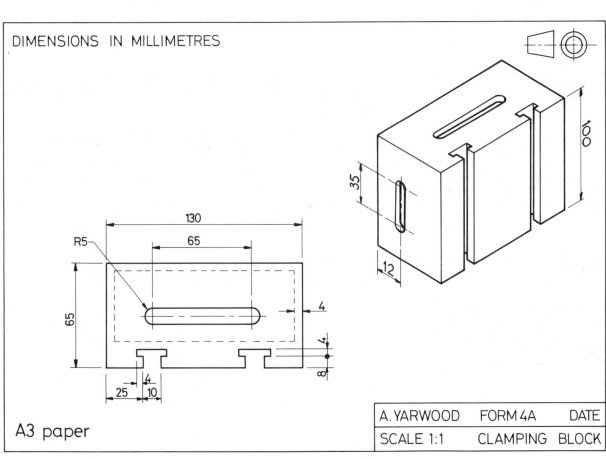

DIMENSIONS IN MILLIMETRES

130
65
R5
65
4
4
8
25
10

35
12
60

A3 paper

| A. YARWOOD | FORM 4A | DATE |
| SCALE 1:1 | CLAMPING BLOCK | |

Angle plate

A photograph and an isometric drawing of an angle plate are shown. This is another device for holding work securely while it is being machined.

Exercise

Prepare a sheet of A3 size paper as shown in the given drawing. Do not copy the isometric drawing.
Copy the given front view.
Add an end view and a plan.
Dimension your drawings.
Include all hidden detail.

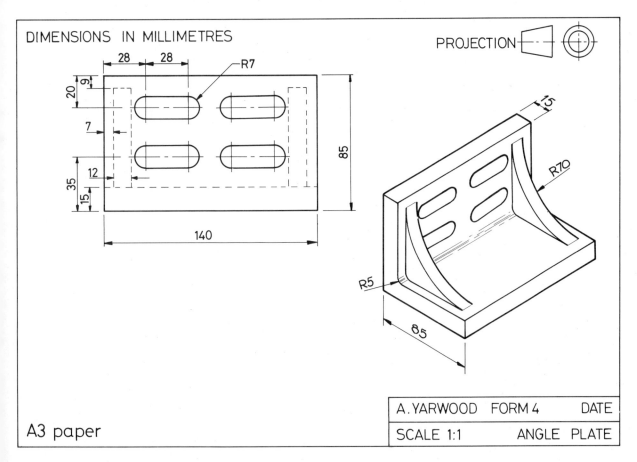

DIMENSIONS IN MILLIMETRES

PROJECTION

28   28   R7

20   9   7

35   12   15

85

140

85

R70

R5

15

A3 paper

A.YARWOOD   FORM 4   DATE

SCALE 1:1   ANGLE PLATE

Towing ball

The photograph shows a 50 mm towing ball bolted to the rear of a car. This is the type of towing hitch commonly used on a family saloon car when it is towing a caravan or a trailer.

A front view and an end view of the towing ball and its bracket are given. The front view is on the right.

Draw the following views of the ball and its brackets:

    (**a**) the given front view,
    (**b**) an end view on the **right** of the front view,
    (**c**) a plan beneath the front view.

Fully dimension the drawing and add a suitable title block. Draw the symbol of projection used near the top of your drawing sheet.

Note: The drawing layout for this towing ball is probably best arranged around centre lines as shown on pages 66 and 67.

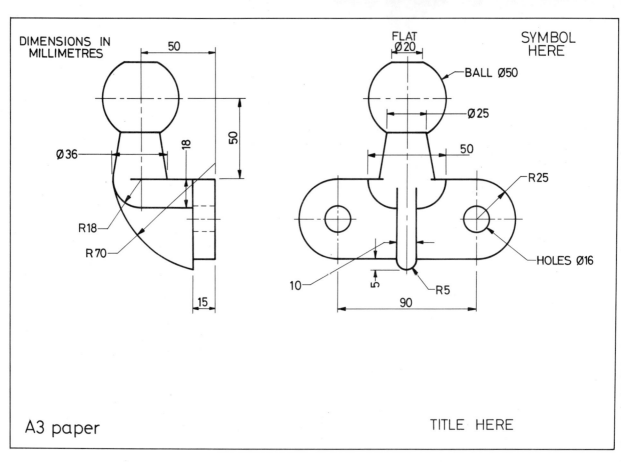

DIMENSIONS IN MILLIMETRES

FLAT Ø20

SYMBOL HERE

BALL Ø50

A3 paper

TITLE HERE

Exercises

1 The drawing shows the plan of a regular hexagonal pyramid of height 50 mm resting on the horizontal plane. Copy the plan and add front and end views. Scale 1:1.

2 Draw a plan view of the component shown, when viewed in the direction of arrow A.   (ALSEB)

3 A front view of a regular hexagonal truncated pyramid is given.
Draw a plan and copy the front view. Draw the end view as seen in the direction of the arrow EV. Scale 1:1.

4 The drawing shows a front view and plan of a regular pentagonal truncated pyramid.
Copy the two views and add an end view as seen from EV.

5 A front view of an equilateral triangular prism is given, together with the true shape of an end. The edge AB is resting on the H.P.
Draw: the given front view, a plan, an end view to the left and an end view to the right.

6 The drawing shows a front view of a regular octagonal pyramid resting on one side on the H.P.
Draw the given view and add an end view to the right and a plan.

3

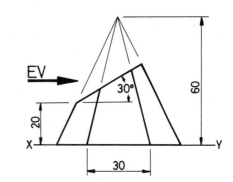

4

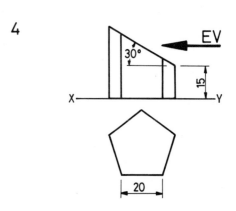

5

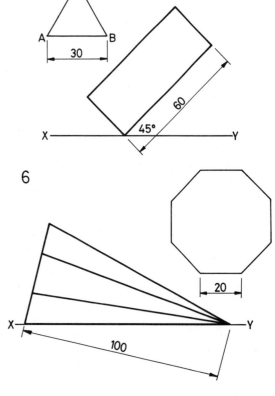

1

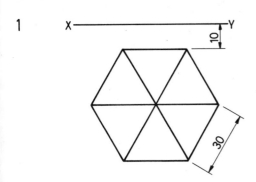

2

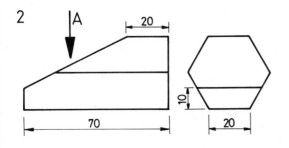

Front view, end view and plan of a hexagonal head ISO metric bolt

See page 110 for further information concerning nuts and bolts.

All the conventions for drawing screw threads shown here are as recommended in British Standards publications. In the stages described below, D is the bolt diameter. See drawing 1.

Stage 1

The Across Flats (A/F) size of the hexagon head is 1.5D.
1. Draw centre lines of the three views.
2. Draw the A/F diameter circle of the end view.
3. Draw a regular hexagon around and touching the circle—use a 30°, 60° set square.
4. Mark off the bolt length.
5. Mark off the bolt head height—0.7D.
6. Project the bolt head faces from the end view on to the head in the front view and plan.
7. Draw the bolt diameter lines.

Stage 2

1. With compasses, draw the arcs on the front view and plan showing the head chamfer.
2. Draw the radius curve at the bolt end.

Stage 3

1. Draw the screw thread as shown.
2. Draw 30° chamfer lines on the front view.
3. Line-in the remainder of the front view and plan.
4. Dimension the screw thread.

Note: When drawing bolts and other screwed parts, it is as well to remember that the methods used are conventions suited to drawing purposes. If exact A/F sizes, thread depths etc. are required, the student must make use of tables such as are found in engineering reference books or in those British Standards which deal with screw threads.

See page 110 for correct recommended methods of dimensioning screw threads.

Exercise

Draw a front view, an end view and a plan of a 75 mm long hexagonal head M20 bolt with a 50 mm length of screw thread.

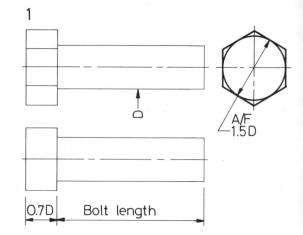

1

0.7D | Bolt length

A/F 1.5 D

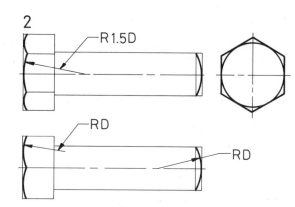

2

R 1.5D

RD

RD

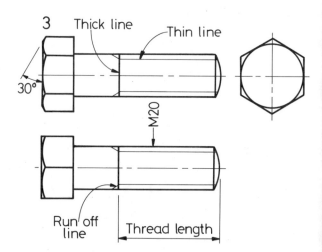

3   Thick line   Thin line

30°

M20

Run off line   Thread length

Three face views of bolt head

Many draughtsmen will show the two-face view of a bolt head by a three-face view. This is a common and generally accepted method used in engineering drawing. It is also common practice not to draw the 30° chamfer lines on the front and end views of a bolt head.

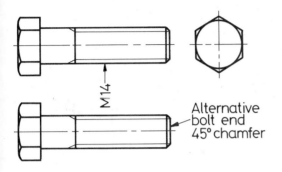

M14

Alternative bolt end 45° chamfer

Hexagonal nut

A three-view First Angle projection of a nut is shown.

Note: The screw thread is a thin line broken in one part.

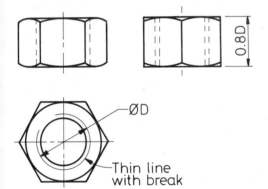

0.8D

ØD

Thin line with break

Front view, end view and plan of a stud

Studs are fixing devices commonly used in engineering. Note the terms used for the various parts of a stud.

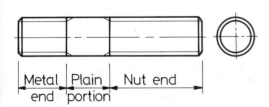

Metal end | Plain portion | Nut end

Washers

Views and details of two types of washer are shown.

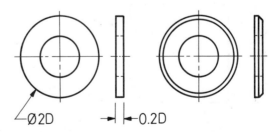

Ø2D   0.2D

Exercises

1 Orthographic views of a portion of aluminium bar are shown. Draw these two views and in consistent projection draw an end elevation viewed in the direction of arrow E. Hidden detail is to be shown. *(North West)*

2 Make a three-view First Angle orthographic projection of the M20 bolt shown.

3 An isometric drawing of an end from a wood-worker's bar cramp is given.
Draw in First Angle projection a front view from the direction of arrow FV, an end view to the left of the front view, and a plan.
You will need a sheet of A3 paper.
Add all dimensions and a title block.

4 Lines are missing in this drawing. It is in First Angle projection.
Complete the drawing by projection from the given views. Hidden detail is to be shown. *(ALSEB)*

5 The isometric drawing shows a fork end.
On an A3 size sheet of paper draw full size in First Angle projection:
  (a) a front view as seen from arrow F,
  (b) end views on both sides of the front view,
  (c) a plan.
Dimension the drawing and add a title block.

2

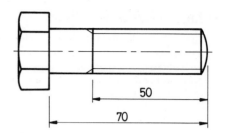

3

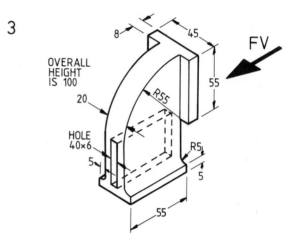

4

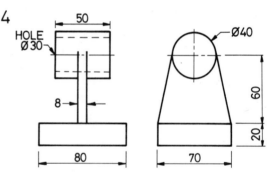

5

1

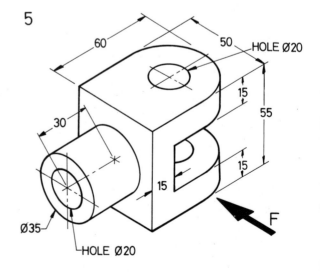

76

First Angle orthographic projection to include a sectional view

1   The drawing shows an object (part of the tool post illustrated on page 55) placed in position on a horizontal plane with two vertical planes, one behind and one to the right of the object.

The object has been cut by a third vertical plane; the part of the object to the left of the cutting V.P. has been removed and the object viewed from the left.

What is seen is projected on to one of the V.P.s as a **sectional end view**.

2   The horizontal and vertical planes have been placed flat and the resulting front view, sectional end view and plan are shown.

Note: A thin chain line thickened at its ends is used to show the edge of the vertical section plane, and arrows touch the thick lines to show the direction in which the cut face is viewed.

The section plane is identified by letters, in this case A–A, and the sectional view is labelled as SECTION A–A.

Not only is the cut face drawn in the sectional end view, but all that can be seen behind the cut face is shown.

The surface which has been cut is **hachured** with thin black lines about 3 to 4 mm apart and at an angle of 45° to the base of the view.

First Angle orthographic projection to include a sectional plan

3   The drawing shows the three viewing planes in position with an object on the horizontal plane.

The object has been cut by a second horizontal plane; the part of the object above the cutting plane has been removed and the object then viewed from above.

What is seen is projected on to the original H.P. as a **sectional plan**.

4   The three planes have been laid flat showing the resulting front view, end view and sectional plan. The section plane is identified by a thick chain line and the letters B–B. The sectional plan is labelled SECTION B–B and the cut face is hachured.

1
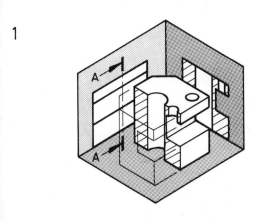

3
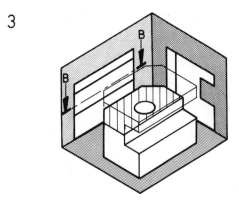

2
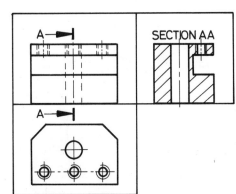

4
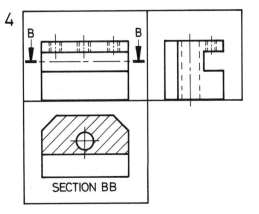

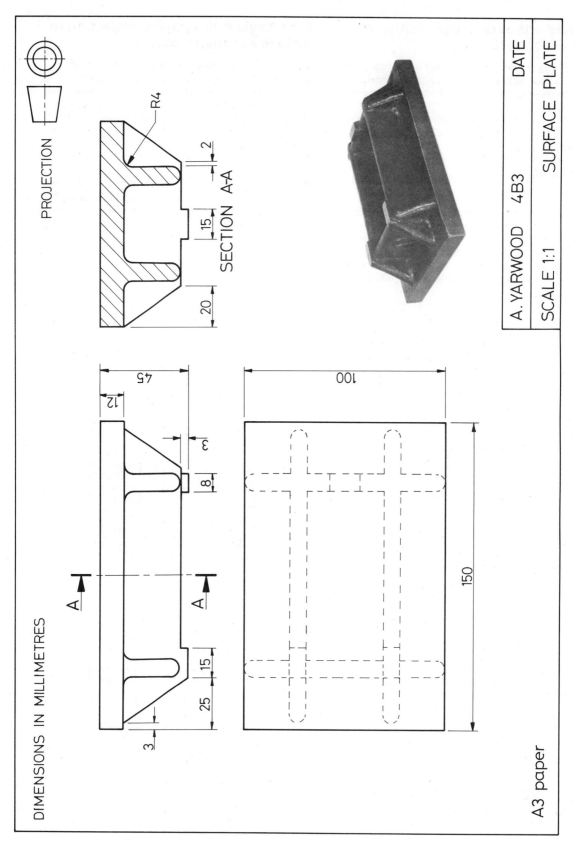

PROJECTION

DIMENSIONS IN MILLIMETRES

R4

SECTION A-A

2

15

20

45

12

3

8

A

A

15

25

3

100

150

A. YARWOOD   4B3   DATE

SCALE 1:1   SURFACE PLATE

A3 paper

Surface plate

The drawing on page 78 opposite shows a front view, sectional end view and a plan in First Angle projection of a small surface plate.

The layout for the drawing is shown on this page in two drawings. This is the fourth type of layout shown in this book and is probably the type most commonly used.

An A3 sheet of paper is needed for this drawing.

1. Draw border lines around the sheet at a distance of 12 mm from each edge.

2. Draw the outline of the title block.

3. Work out the vertical spacing for the layout on a piece of scrap paper. Attempt equal divisions between the drawings and between drawings and lettering. Draw fine construction lines.

4. Work out the horizontal spacing and draw fine construction lines. This gives the positioning of the three views.

5. Fill in details of the three views using fine construction lines – 2H pencil.

6. Line-in all arcs using an H or HB lead in the compasses.

7. Line-in all straight lines – 2H pencil.

8. Draw guide lines for lettering, include the label SECTION A–A, 4 mm for lettering along top edge, 5 or 6 mm for title and SECTION A–A.

9. Fill in all lettering using an H or HB pencil.

10. Draw dimension lines, dimension projection lines, hidden detail and hachure lines with fine black lines drawn with a 2H pencil. Add arrow heads with H or HB pencil.

11. Fill in dimensions.

12. Rub out unwanted construction lines.

Notes
1. Hachure lines on cut surface of sectional end view.
2. Thick chain line and arrows showing section plane.
3. The label SECTION A–A.
These three details should be included in drawings which include sectional views.

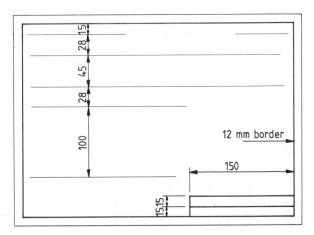

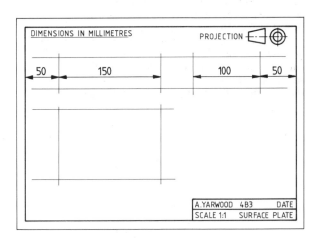

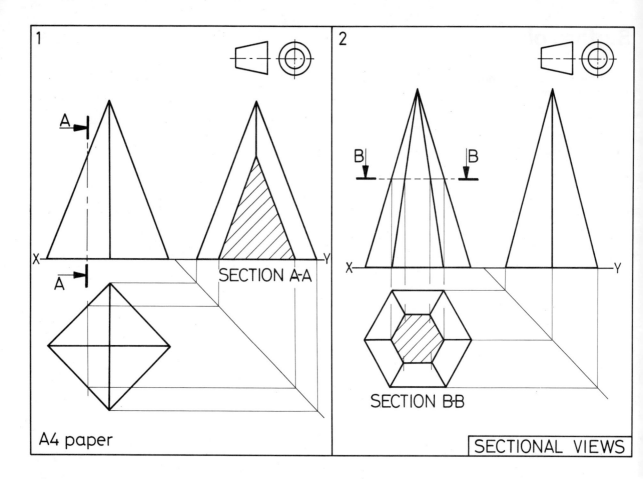

SECTION A-A

A4 paper

SECTION B-B

SECTION VIEWS

1 Front view, plan and sectional end view in First Angle projection of a square pyramid

Edges of base are each 40 mm long.

Vertical height of pyramid is 70 mm.

Section plane 10 mm to left of centre of pyramid.

Draw the plan and the front view in that order.

Draw the section plane chain line.

Project the sectional end view as shown from the plan and the front view.

Label the ends of the section plane edge and the sectional end view.

Hachure the cut surface of the sectional view.

2 Front view, end view and sectional plan in First Angle projection of a regular hexagonal pyramid

Edges of hexagonal base are each 25 mm long.

Vertical height of pyramid is 80 mm.

Horizontal section plane 40 mm vertically above H.P.

Construct the full plan, front view and end view.

Draw the section plane and project from the points where the plane cuts the sloping edges of the pyramid down to the plan to obtain the shape of the cut surface in the plan.

Complete the drawing by lining-in and add lettering as shown, including X and Y on the base line.

Exercises

1 The section A–A through a square based pyramid is unfinished. Complete this view.

2 The sphere is cut by a plane. Draw the section L–L.

3 A front view of regular octagonal pyramid cut centrally by a section plane B–B. Draw the section B–B.

4 A front view of a regular hexagonal pyramid of base edge lengths 20 mm is cut by the section plane C–C as shown.
Draw a front view, an end view and the sectional plan C–C.

5 A front view and an incomplete plan of a pentagonal pyramid are shown. The pyramid is cut by section plane D–D sloping at 30° to the H.P.
Draw the given front view, complete the plan and add the sectional view D–D.

6 A cube is shown in front view resting on the H.P. Draw this view, add a plan and the sectional view E–E.

7 A cylinder is shown resting on the H.P. and cut by section plane P–P.
Draw the given front view, add an end view and the sectional plan P–P.

8 An equilateral triangular prism of length 50 mm and triangle side lengths 20 mm rests at an angle of 45° on a cube of 30 mm edge length.
Draw the front view, add a complete plan and the sectional end view S–S.

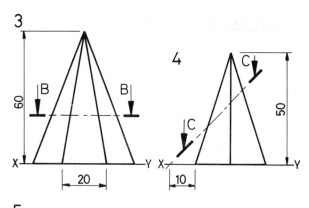

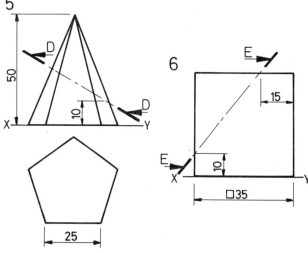

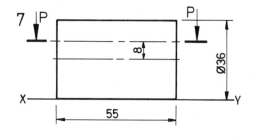

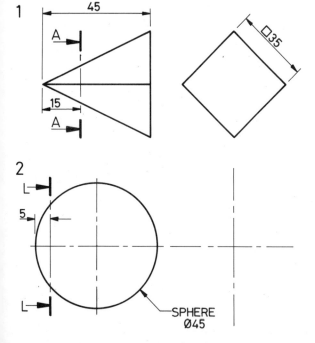

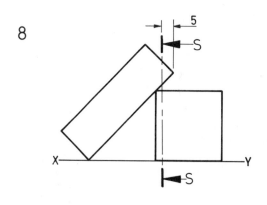

81

Exercises

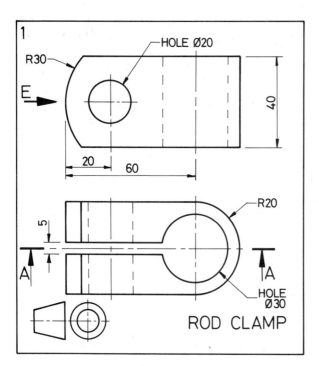

ROD CLAMP

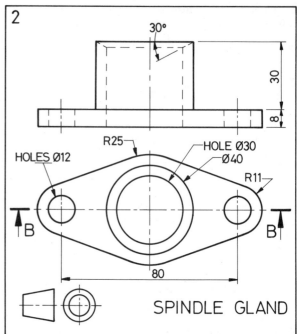

SPINDLE GLAND

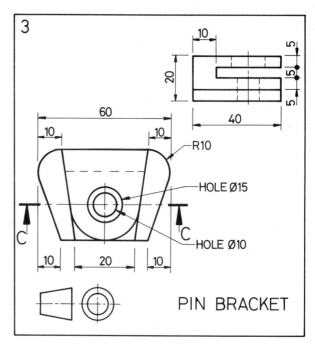

PIN BRACKET

1 Two views of a rod clamp are given. Working to a scale of 1:1:
   (**a**) draw the given plan,
   (**b**) project from the plan the sectional view A–A,
   (**c**) add an end view as seen in the direction of the arrow E.
Use an A4 sheet of drawing paper. Include a title block, the symbol of projection and five main dimensions.

2 A front view and a plan of a spindle gland are shown. Use an A4 sheet of drawing paper. Draw border lines, a title block and the symbol of projection.
Draw scale 1:1:
   (**a**) the given plan,
   (**b**) the sectional front view B–B,
   (**c**) an end view.
Fully dimension your drawing.

3 A plan and an end view of a pin bracket are given. Use an A4 size sheet of paper. Draw, scale 1:1:
   (**a**) the two given views,
   (**b**) the sectional front view C–C.
Include the following in your drawing:
   (**i**) five dimensions,
   (**ii**) a title block,
   (**iii**) the symbol of projection,
   (**iv**) the unit of dimensioning.

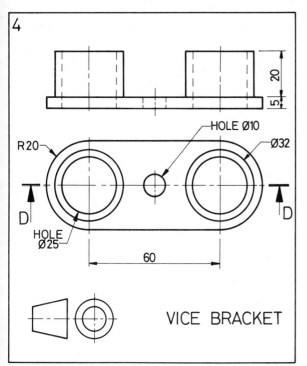

VICE BRACKET

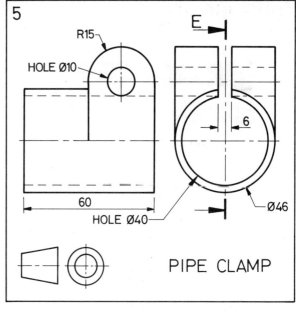

PIPE CLAMP

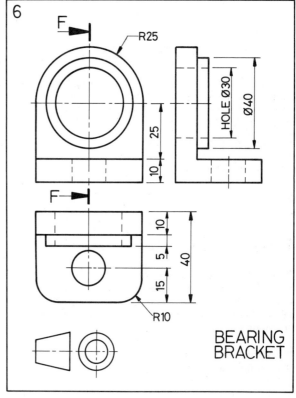

BEARING BRACKET

4 A front view and plan of a vice bracket are given. Use an A4 sheet of drawing paper. Draw, scale 1:1, the following views of the bracket:
    (a) the sectional front view D–D,
    (b) a plan,
    (c) an end view.
Fully dimension your drawing and add a title block.

5 Front and end views of a pipe clamp are shown. Use an A4 sheet of paper. Draw, scale 1:1:
    (a) the given end view,
    (b) the sectional front view E–E,
    (c) a plan.
Dimension your drawing and add a title block.

6 Three views of a bearing bracket are given. On an A4 sheet of paper draw, scale 1:1:
    (a) the given front view and plan,
    (b) the sectional end view F–F.
Add a title and dimension your drawing.

Bolts and screws

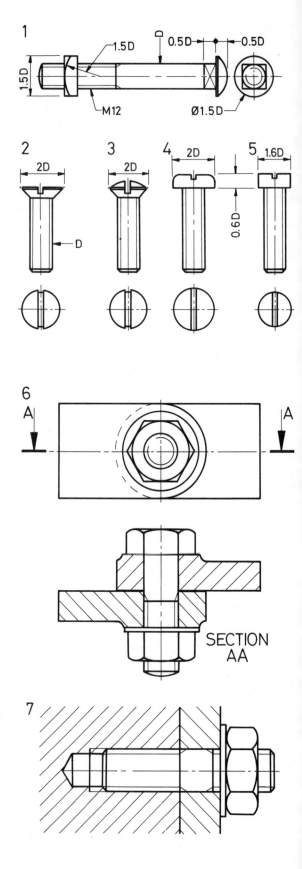

It is generally agreed that the thread of a machine screw is machined along the entire length of its diameter whereas a bolt has a plain portion between its head and the start of its thread.

1 Front and end views of a coach bolt. The front view shows a square nut in position. The end view has been drawn without the nut.

2 A countersunk head machine screw.

3 A raised countersunk head machine screw.

4 A pan head machine screw.

5 A cheese head machine screw.
British Standard 308 *Engineering Drawing Practice* states: 'In principle, ribs, bolts, shafts, spokes of wheels and the like should not be shown in longitudinal section.' Drawings 6 and 7 show two applications of this rule.

6 A front view and sectional plan through a bolt and nut holding two parts together.

7 A sectional view through a stud and nut holding two parts together.

Note: In drawings 6 and 7 the bolt, stud, nuts and washers are shown by outside views. In both cases the washer is placed under that part of the fastening which is turned to tighten the parts together.

Exercises

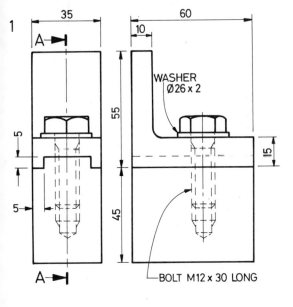

1

A ►

35

10

60

WASHER
Ø26 x 2

55

5

15

45

5

A ►

BOLT M12 x 30 LONG

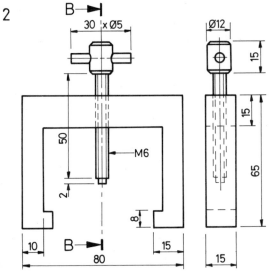

2

B ►

30 x Ø5

Ø12

15

15

50

M6

65

2

8

10

B ►

15

80

15

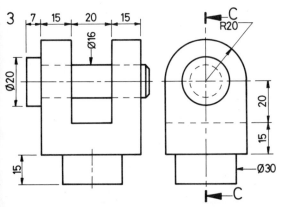

3

7 15 20 15

Ø16

Ø20

15

C
R20

20

15

Ø30

C

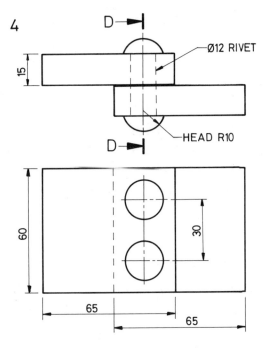

4

D ►

Ø12 RIVET

15

HEAD R10

D ►

60

30

65

65

1 A front view and an end view of two parts of a fitting joined together with a bolt and washer are given. They are drawn in First Angle projection.
The left-hand view is the end view.
Use an A4 sheet of drawing paper.
Copy the given end view. Add the sectional front view taken on the sectional plane A–A. Add a plan.
Work to a scale of 1:1.

2 Front and end views in First Angle projection of a V block clamp are given. Use an A4 sheet of paper. Copy the given front view, add the sectional end view B–B and a plan. Work to a scale of 1:1.

3 Front and end views of a fork coupling are given. They are drawn in First Angle projection. Use an A4 sheet of paper. Copy the given end view, and add a sectional front view C–C and a plan. Scale 1:1.

4 A First Angle front view and a plan of two pieces of metal riveted together by two round head rivets are shown. Use an A4 sheet of paper. Copy the two given views and add the Sectional end view D–D. Scale 1:1.

DIMENSIONS IN MILLIMETRES

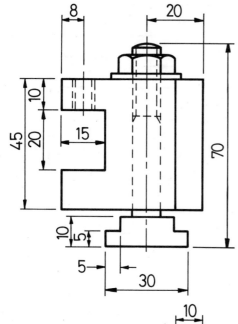

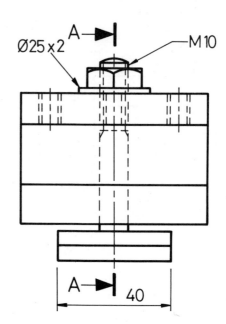

Ø25 x 2

A

M 10

A

40

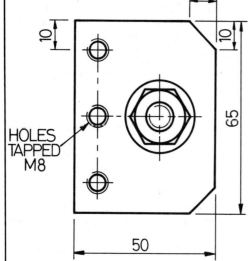

HOLES
TAPPED
M8

10

65

50

A4 paper

Exercises

1   The photograph shows an English type lathe tool post. The drawing on page 86 opposite is a First Angle projection of the tool post. The bolts for holding the tool in position have been removed.

Do not copy the three views

Use an A4 sheet of paper.

Draw, scale 1:1, the following three views:

     (**a**) the given end view as a front view,

     (**b**) a plan beneath this new front view,

     (**c**) the sectional end view A–A.

Fully dimension the drawing, add a title block and show the form of projection used.

2   A front view and plan of a clip bolt are shown. Copy the two given views, scale 1:1, and add the sectional view B–B.

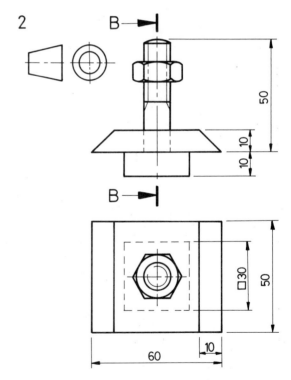

Tension testing device

A photograph of part of the handle of a tension testing device is given, together with three views in First Angle orthographic projection of the clamp from the handle.

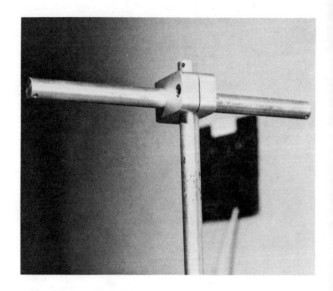

Exercise

Working to a scale of 1:1, copy the given front view and plan and, in place of the given end view, draw the sectional view A–A.

Add a title block to your drawing and add the main dimensions to the views.

All three views should include the hexagonal socket bolt screwed fully home into its hole.

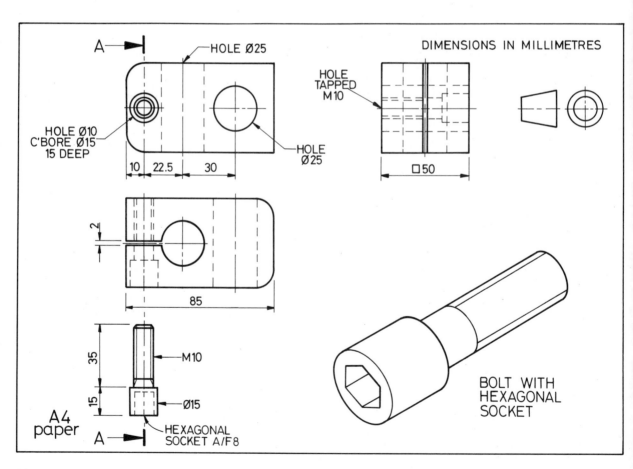

DIMENSIONS IN MILLIMETRES

HOLE Ø25

HOLE TAPPED M10

HOLE Ø10 C'BORE Ø15 15 DEEP

HOLE Ø25

10   22.5   30

□50

2

85

35

M10

15

Ø15

A4 paper

HEXAGONAL SOCKET A/F8

BOLT WITH HEXAGONAL SOCKET

Adjusting clamp

The photograph shows an adjusting clamp from a drill stand designed to hold a small power drill. A three-view orthographic drawing of the parts of the clamp is also given. Part 1 is a bolt, Part 2 is a nut, Part 3 is a pin and Part 4 the body of the clamp.

Exercise

Draw, scale 1:1, the following three views of the **assembled** clamp, with the bolt, nut and pin positioned in the body:

    (**a**) in place of the given front view the sectional view A–A,

    (**b**) the given end view,

    (**c**) the given plan.

Add a title block to your drawing, the symbol of projection and a statement showing the unit of dimensioning.

Include five main dimensions to your drawing.

Note the lines showing **straight knurling** on the bolt head.

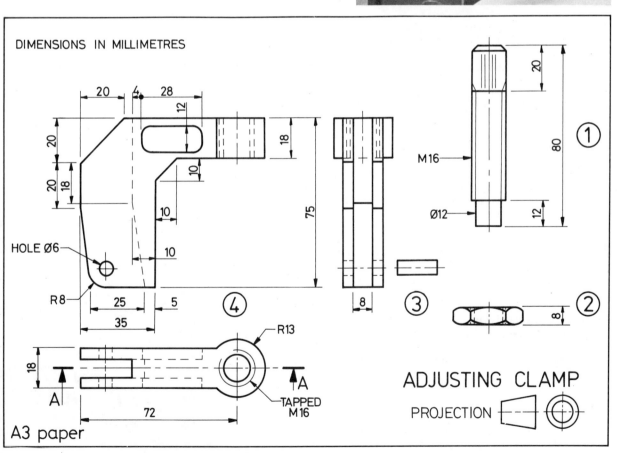

DIMENSIONS IN MILLIMETRES

HOLE Ø6

R8

M 16

Ø12

R13

TAPPED M 16

A3 paper

ADJUSTING CLAMP

PROJECTION

89

Freehand sketching

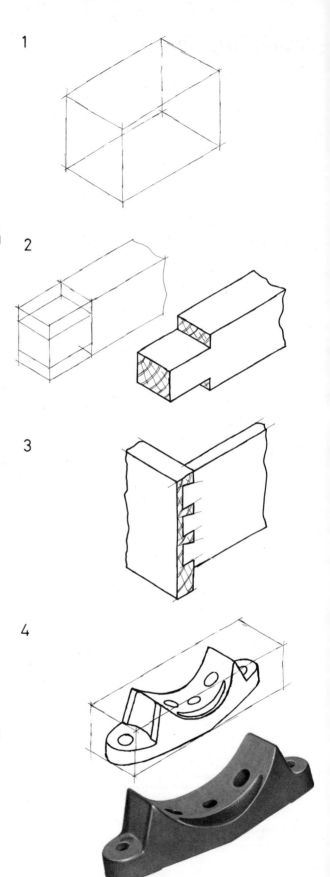

An important part of Technical Drawing is the freehand sketching of objects associated with the drawings a draughtsman is called upon to make. Such sketches may need to be made of the whole of the object being drawn; of parts such as joints and small details; of tools associated with the making of the object; or as sketches made in preparation for the drawing of orthographic projections.

The student is advised to make sketches as simple as possible and to avoid all forms of shading. Until some considerable degree of ability in sketching is achieved by constant practice, it is better to make line sketches, based either on approximate isometric drawing or on orthographic projection views.

1 The construction outline of a small block sketched on approximate isometric lines—the uprights are approximately vertical on the page and the sloping lines are at approximately 30° to the horizontal. Such a construction outline should be used in a similar manner as when making an isometric drawing—the block contains the overall sizes of the object being sketched.

2 A stub tenon cut in the end of a piece of wood of section 30 mm by 20 mm. The tenon is 20 mm long by 16 mm thick.
The left-hand sketch shows the end of the piece of wood sketched in outline on approximate isometric lines, with the detail of the tenon sketched in ready for finishing the sketch. Construction lines have been drawn with a sharp HB pencil.
The right-hand sketch shows the completed sketch lined in with an HB pencil. Unnecessary construction has been erased.
It is customary to show end grain on sketches of wooden detail. This indicates the grain direction. The growth rings and medullary rays are shown. The far end of the wood has been sketched as if broken off.

3 A lap dovetail joint as used in a drawer side-to-front joint. The completed sketch, before rubbing out construction lines which are not needed, is shown.

4 A sketch of a stand in which a pipe, such as a heavy central heating pipe, is clamped. Note the lack of shading and the use again of approximate isometric axes. Part of the construction block in which the sketch was made has been shown.

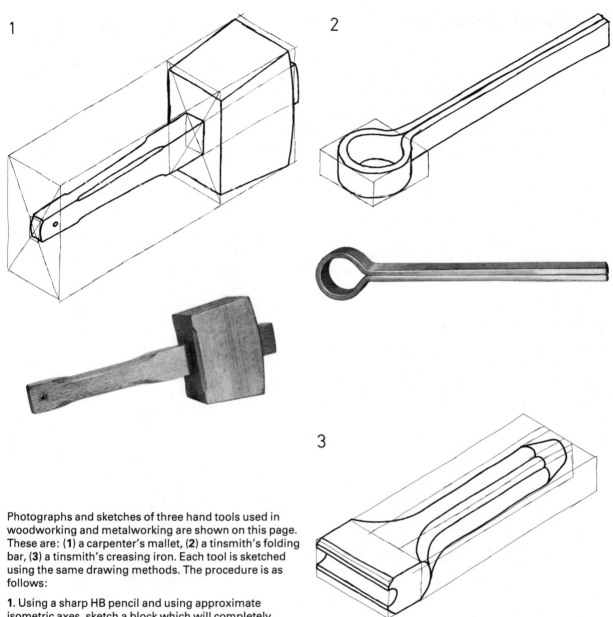

Photographs and sketches of three hand tools used in woodworking and metalworking are shown on this page. These are: (**1**) a carpenter's mallet, (**2**) a tinsmith's folding bar, (**3**) a tinsmith's creasing iron. Each tool is sketched using the same drawing methods. The procedure is as follows:

1. Using a sharp HB pencil and using approximate isometric axes, sketch a block which will completely contain the tool. The proportions of the block should be drawn as near to those of the tool as can be estimated.

2. Locate any major features within the block outline such as the ends of the handle of the carpenter's mallet.

3. Sketch in all the details of the various features of the tool ensuring these details are in reasonable proportion to the remainder of the sketch.

4. Line in the outline of the tool and its various parts with clean firm lines using an HB pencil.

5. Using a clean pencil eraser, erase any unwanted construction.

Freehand sketching

Freehand sketches may be drawn in preparation for orthographic projections. Three examples are given. Sketches similar to these examples can be made:

(**a**) as a preparation for an orthographic projection of the object in order to work out layout and to check that detail has not been missed from the finished drawing, or

(**b**) to make a quick sketch of an object from which a final drawing can be made when the object is no longer available.

Such drawings need not be very large. Some students may find that an exercise book, particularly one ruled with square graph lines, can be used for such preparatory sketching.

1 A freehand sketch made in preparation for drawing a three-view orthographic projection of an audio cassette player.

2 A three-view freehand orthographic projection of a guide from a mortising machine.

3 A freehand sketch of a switch from the electricity circuitry of a machine shop.

Note: Freehand sketches drawn on orthographic principles of projection may be dimensioned or not, depending upon the use for which the drawing is being made.

2

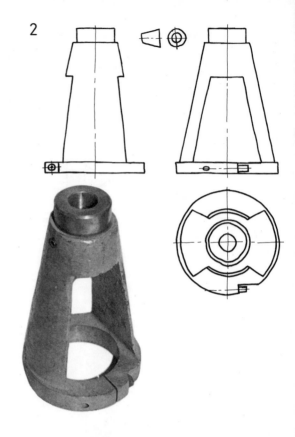

1

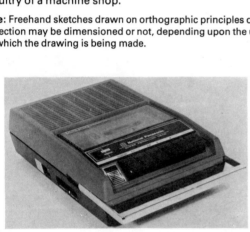

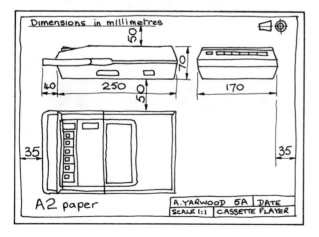

3

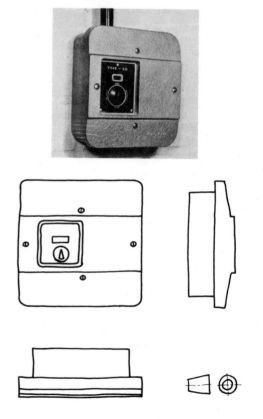

Exercises

1 Draw a freehand pictorial sketch of the model shown. Hidden detail should not be shown. Sketches should be in good proportion. (*ALSEB*)

2 Draw a freehand pictorial sketch of the model shown. Hidden detail should not be shown. Sketches should be in good proportion. (*ALSEB*)

3 The sketch shows a holder for a clothes line post. The holder is bolted to a concrete foundation through the four holes. The hole to contain the post stops at the level of the top surface of the supports.
Sketch the following views of the casting, obtaining your dimensions by measuring the given sketch:
    (**a**) a sectional view on B–B,
    (**b**) a plan.
Fillets are not shown but you are to put them in your drawing where you consider they should appear.

4 Draw a freehand pictorial sketch of the model shown. Hidden detail should not be shown. Sketches should be in good proportion. (*ALSEB*)

5 The figure shows the base of a scribing block. Draw the following views, freehand and full size, of the block:
    (**a**) a sectional view along S–S,
    (**b**) an end view taken in the direction of the arrow P,
    (**c**) a plan.
Show hidden detail in (b) and (c).

2
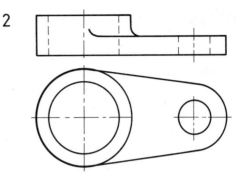

3
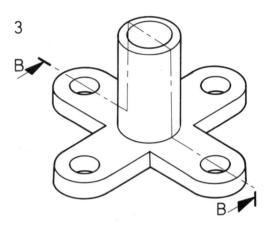

4
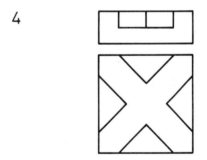

1
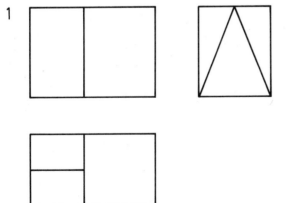

5
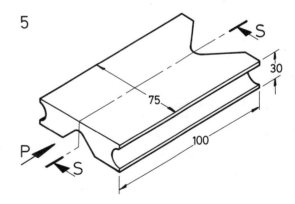

Exercises

1 The drawing shows a front view and plan in first angle projection of an aluminium casting which is to be machined into a head for a cine-camera.
Make a *freehand* sketch of the casting. Do not show hidden detail.

2 First Angle projection – paper punch handle.
Do not copy the given views.
Draw *freehand* a pictorial sketch of the handle.
The corner A should be the lowest point on your drawing.
Do not show hidden detail.

3 First Angle projection – pulley on spindle.
Copy the given drawing *freehand* and complete the sectional view A–A. Do not include hidden detail.

4 The drawing shows a special flanged pipe.
Copy the two given views *freehand* and add a plan view in section on A–A.

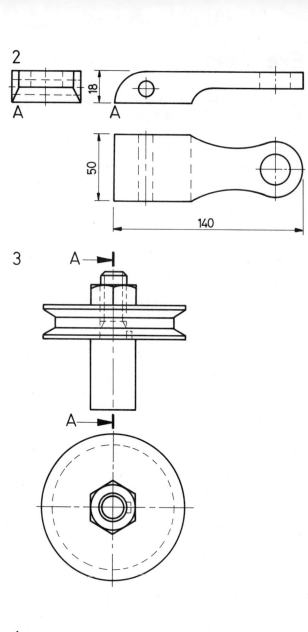

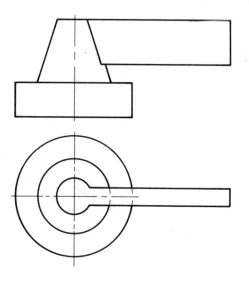

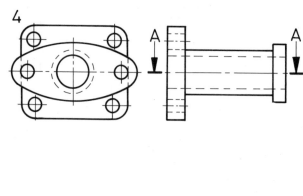

5

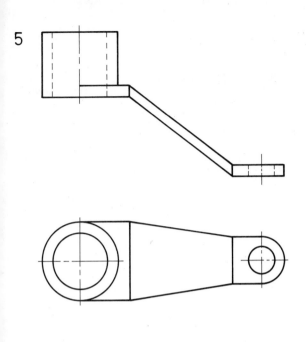

6

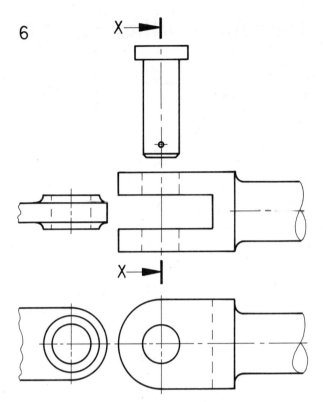

5 Selector arm – Draw *freehand* a pictorial sketch.

6 Details of a connecting rod joint are given. With the joint assembled, draw *freehand*, a sectional view on X–X.

7 A plan and sectional front view of a valve are given. Draw *freehand* an outside view of the valve.

Note: In this example the web of the valve is shown by an outside view. This method of showing webs in section is the correct method and will be shown again in Book 2.

7

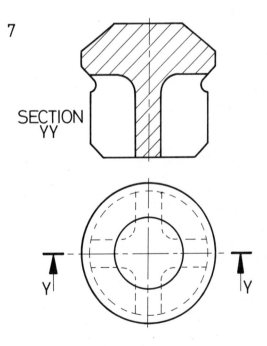

SECTION YY

Third Angle orthographic projection

1   Drawing 1 is a repeat of the drawing of orthogonal planes given on page 55. The drawing shows the position of the Third Angle.

2   In Third Angle projection the object to be drawn is suspended in the third angle between the H.P. and the V.P. The object is viewed **through** the V.P. and what is seen then drawn on the V.P. This gives a **front view**. The object is also viewed **through** the H.P. and what is seen drawn on the H.P. This gives a **plan**.

3   The H.P. and V.P. are rotated so as to lie in the same flat plane. The result is an orthographic projection in **Third Angle**.

4   The **symbol** for Third Angle orthographic projection is a Third Angle orthographic projection of the frustum of a cone.

Notes
1. The plan of the object is **above** the front view in Third angle projection.
2. The plan is facing towards the front view. The front edge of the plan is the edge nearest to the front view.
3. The student is advised to learn how to draw views in Third Angle projection. The two types of orthographic projection – First Angle and Third Angle – are of equal importance.

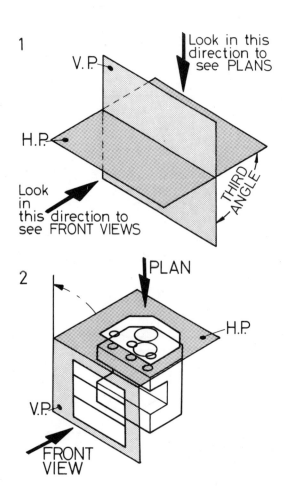

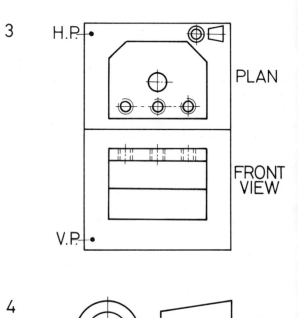

Third Angle orthographic projection

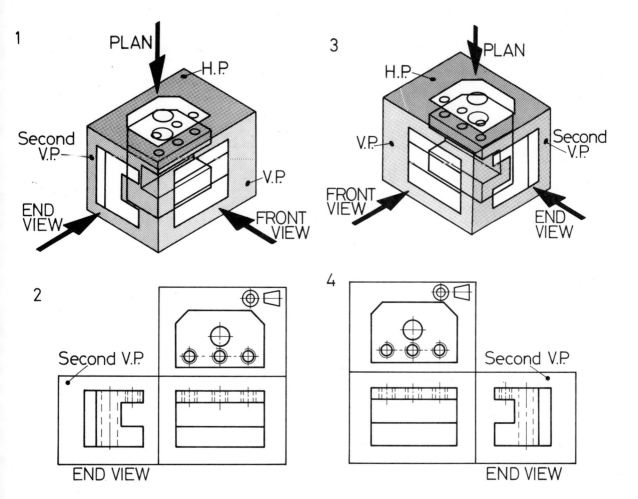

If an end view of an object is required a second V.P. can be placed, either to the left of the first V.P. or to the right.

1 A second vertical plane placed to the left of the object being drawn. The object is viewed **through** the second V.P. and what is seen then drawn on the second V.P.

2 All three planes – the H.P., the V.P. and the second V.P. are rotated so that they all lie in the same flat plane. Note that in this example the end view is to the left of the front view.

3 A second vertical plane placed to the right of the object being drawn. The object is viewed through the second V.P. and what is seen is drawn on the second V.P.

4 All three planes are rotated so as to lie in the same flat plane. Note that in this example the end view is drawn to the right of the front view.

Notes
1. The end view, whether drawn to the left or to the right of the front view, is drawn so as to face **towards** the front view.
2. If the end view is obtained by viewing the front view from the left, then the end view is drawn to the left of the front view.
3. If the end view is obtained by viewing the front view from the right, then the end view is drawn to the right of the front view.

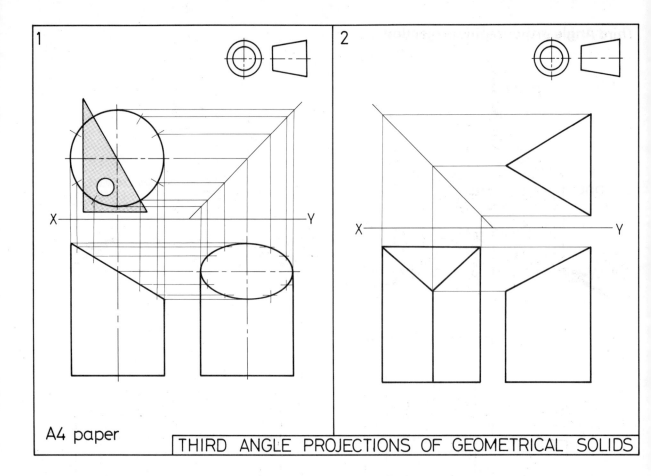

THIRD ANGLE PROJECTIONS OF GEOMETRICAL SOLIDS

A4 paper

1 Truncated cylinder

Cylinder diameter 40 mm, maximum height 60 mm, truncation at 30° to horizontal.

The method shown is similar to that used in First Angle projection.

Note that the front view does not touch the XY line.

To plot the ellipse on the end view

(a) Divide the plan into 12 equal parts (30°, 60° set square).

(b) Project each of these 12 points of division from the plan on to the front view and end view.

(c) Project the points of division from the front view on to the end view.

(d) The ellipse is drawn through the points of intersection of the two sets of projection lines from the plan and the front view.

2 Truncated triangular prism

Triangle of equilateral sides 45 mm long, long edges of prism are 60 mm long, short edge is 40 mm long.

The drawing of the three views follows on work already shown in projecting views.

Note: The plan should be drawn first. The end view is to the left of the front view.

Exercises

Copy the two given examples.

Worked example – Third Angle projection

A photograph of an angle plate is given together with a three-view Third Angle orthographic projection of the plate.

Exercise

Use an A3 size sheet of paper.
Work the spacings for the three views on a scrap of paper.
Copy the given drawing.
Include the dimensions, title block, symbol of projection and dimensioning units statement.

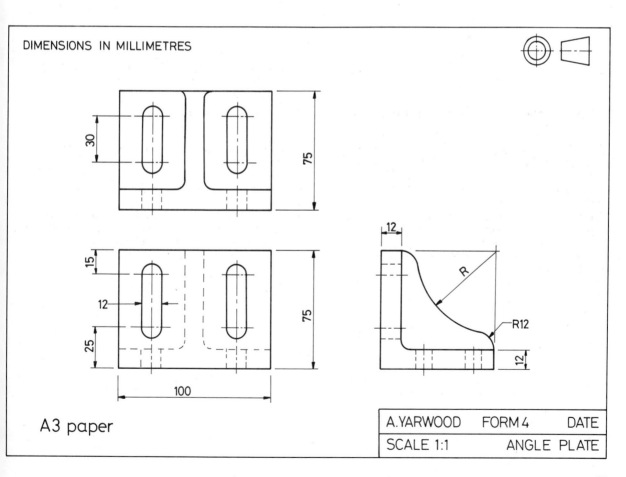

DIMENSIONS IN MILLIMETRES

30
75
15
12
25
12
100

12
R
R12
12
75

A3 paper

A.YARWOOD	FORM 4	DATE
SCALE 1:1		ANGLE PLATE

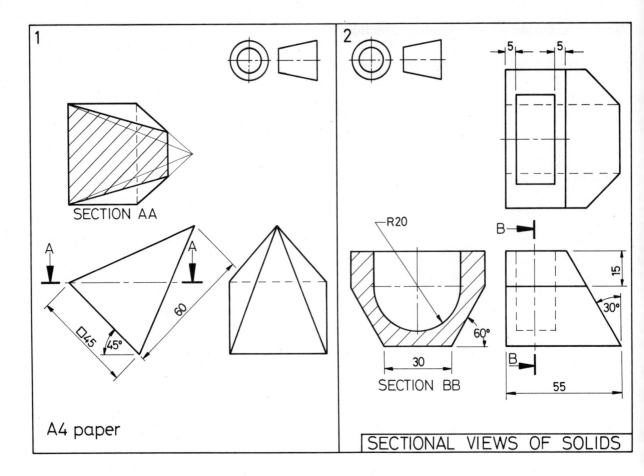

A4 paper

SECTIONAL VIEWS OF SOLIDS

Worked examples – Third Angle projections including sections

1 A three-view drawing in Third Angle projection of a square pyramid tilted at an angle of 45° to the horizontal plane.

Draw the front view to the sizes given. The sectional plane A–A is horizontal.

Project the end view from the front view.

Project the complete plan, before being sectioned, from the front and end views.

Add the cut surface of the section A–A to the plan.

Include the symbol of projection.

2 A three-view drawing of a prism, truncated at one end, and containing a rectangular slot with a semi-circular bottom.

Copy the three views. It is best to commence with the outline of the sectional end view B–B, followed by the front view and then projecting the plan from the front and end views. Finally complete details of the sectional view B–B, and add hatching lines and hidden detail.

Include the symbol of projection.

Third Angle projection of a casting box handle

A photograph of a casting box handle is shown together with a complete Third Angle projection of the handle. The projection includes a sectional end view.

Exercise

Use an A3 size sheet of drawing paper.
Work out the position of the views on a scrap piece of paper.
Copy the given drawing.
Include a title, all dimensions, the symbol of projection and the dimensioning units statement.

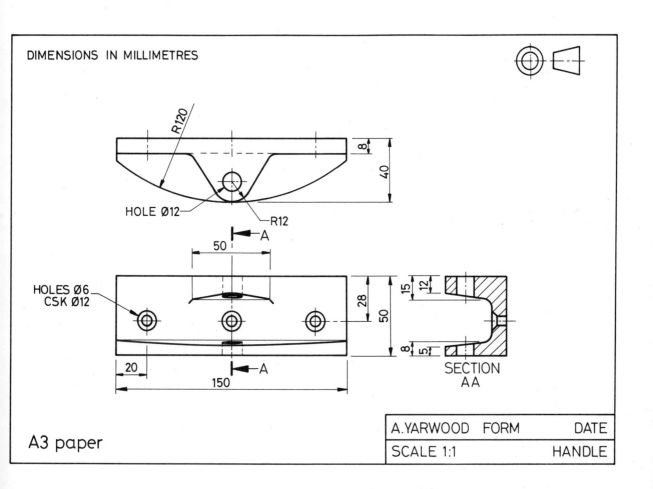

DIMENSIONS IN MILLIMETRES

R120
HOLE Ø12
R12
8
40
50

A
50
HOLES Ø6
CSK Ø12
28
50
15
12
8
5
20
150
A

SECTION
AA

A3 paper

A.YARWOOD   FORM   DATE
SCALE 1:1   HANDLE

Exercises

1 Sketch in good proportion, in Third Angle projection, the three views indicated by the letters F, E and P.
(*North Western*)

2 Sketch in good proportion, in Third Angle projection, the three views indicated by the letters F, E and P.
(*North Western*)

3 Third Angle projection. Draw the third principal view.
(*Welsh*)

4 Third Angle projection. Add the third principal view.
(*Welsh*)

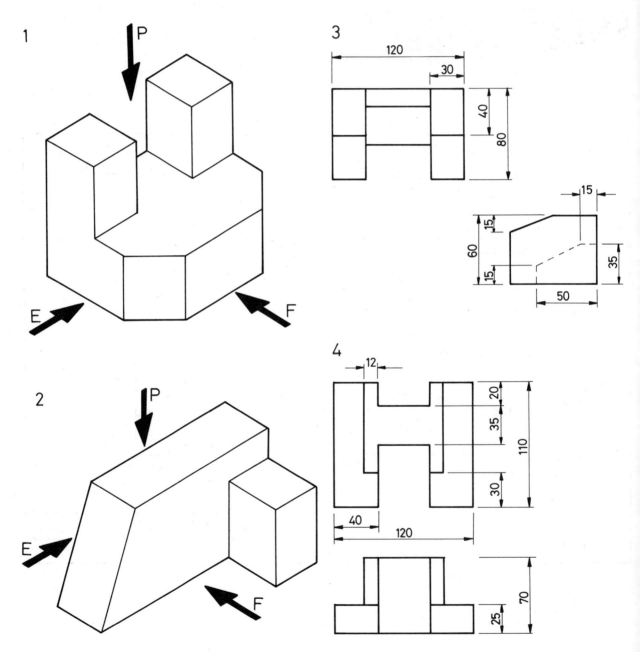

5

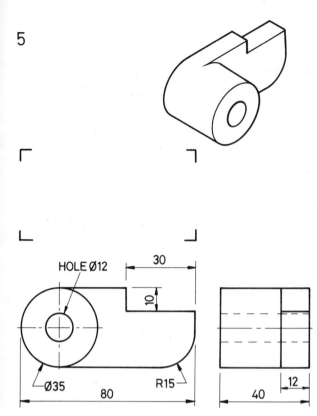

HOLE Ø12
30
10
Ø35
80
R15
40
12

6

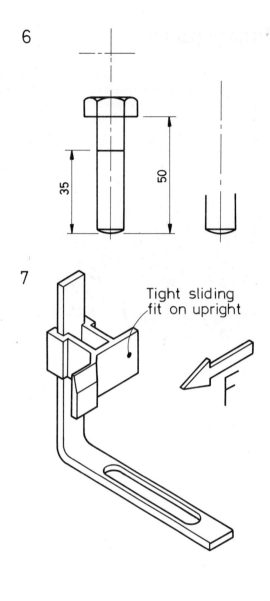

35
50

7

Tight sliding fit on upright

F

8

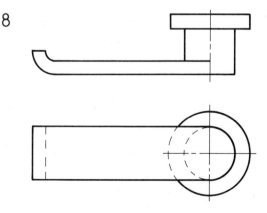

5 Two incomplete views in Third Angle orthographic projection are given. Complete these views by adding the centre lines and draw a plan view in the space provided. Add six dimensions in millimetres, which must include a radius and a diameter. *(East Anglian, South)*

6 The partly finished front view of an M12 bolt is given. Complete this view by adding lines to represent the thread, and draw the end elevation and plan. *(East Anglian, South)*

7 A drawing of an adjustable stop from a machine is given. Draw *freehand* in Third Angle orthographic projection, approximately scale 1:1, the following three views of the adjustable stop:
    (**a**) a front view as seen in the direction of the arrow F,
    (**b**) the end view which shows the most details,
    (**c**) a plan.
Hidden detail is not required.
Add the symbol of projection to your drawing.
Your drawings *must* be freehand and *must* be in Third Angle projection. *(London)*

8 Door handle casting – Third Angle projection. Draw a pictorial *freehand* sketch to the same scale as the given views. *(West Midlands)*

Pulley guard

A photograph of a pulley guard from a machine is given. An isometric drawing of the guard as seen from the rear is also shown. On page 105 opposite a fully dimensioned front view of the guard has been drawn.

Note that the front faces of the guard are 5 mm thick, in which thickness recesses 2 mm deep are cut as shown.

Exercise

On an A3 sheet of paper draw, scale 1:1, in Third Angle projection:
   (a) the given front view,
   (b) the sectional end view A–A in the position indicated,
   (c) a plan in the position indicated,
Add to your drawing:
   (i)   five main dimensions,
   (ii) a title block,
   (iii) the symbol of projection,
   (iv) the statement DIMENSIONS IN MILLIMETRES.

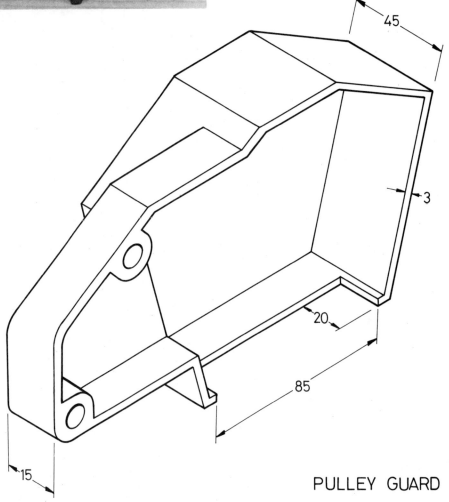

PULLEY GUARD

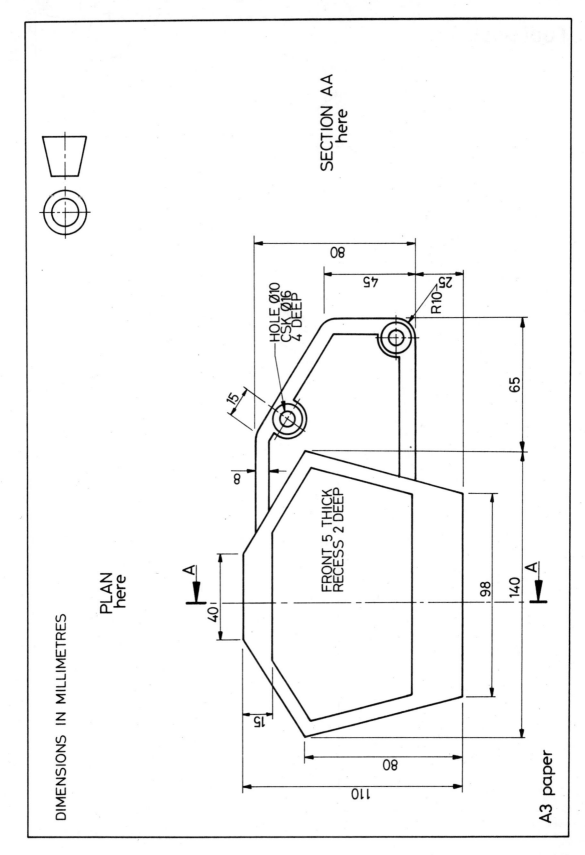

DIMENSIONS IN MILLIMETRES

PLAN
here

SECTION AA
here

HOLE Ø10
CSK Ø16
4 DEEP

FRONT 5 THICK
RECESS 2 DEEP

R10

15

8

80

45

25

65

40

98

140

15

80

110

A3 paper

A

A

Tool post

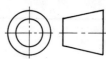

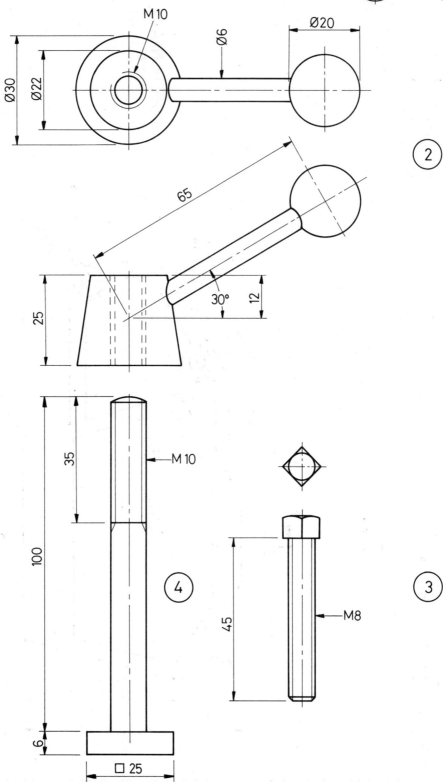

M 10

Ø30

Ø22

Ø6

Ø20

②

65

25

30°

12

35

M 10

④

100

6

□ 25

③

M8

45

The drawings on this page and on page 106 opposite should be read together. They are in Third Angle projection.

The drawings show the four parts of a lathe tool post and a sketch intended as a guide to show how the parts are assembled.

You are required to do the following:

(a) Complete the two elevations by adding the three remaining parts to make the assembly. Sizes can be taken from the drawings.

The central bolt should be shown with its end radius only visible. Only *one* set screw need to be drawn, as shown in the sketch.

(b) Project a plan.
(c) Print the title.
(d) Dimension the block to show its length, width and height.

Hidden detail is required in both elevations but not in the plan. All dimensions are in millimetres. (*West Midlands*)

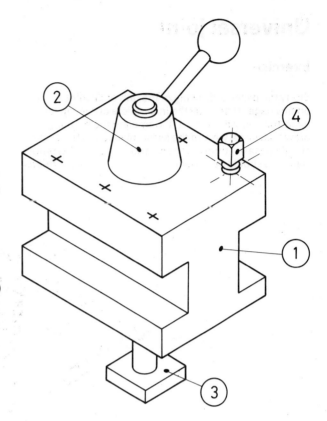

ITEM No.	NAME	MATL	No. off
1	BODY	M.S. C.H.	1
2	BALL HANDLE	M.S.	1
3	CENTRAL BOLT	M.S. C.H.	1
4	SET SCREW	M.S.	4

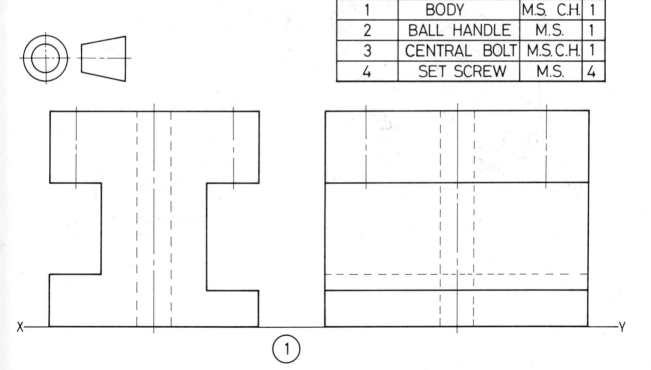

Universal joint

Exercise

Study the pictorial drawing of the universal joint shown on this page. Then copy the incomplete outline given on page 109 opposite, scale 1:1. Complete the partially drawn sectional view of the assembled joint. The section should be taken through the central axis of the assembly. Hatching should be shown.   (*South-East*)

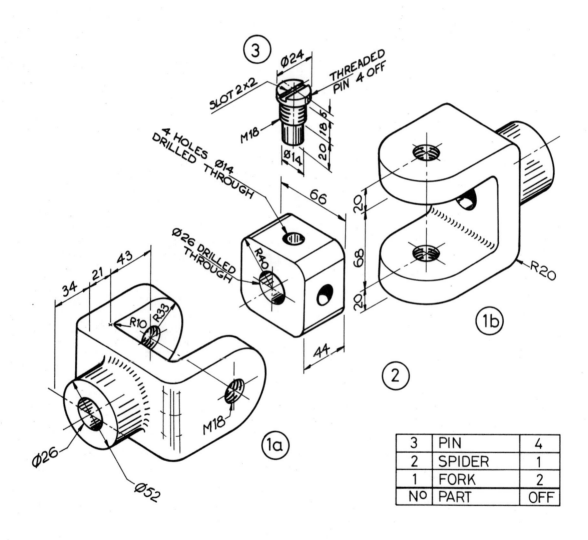

3	PIN	4
2	SPIDER	1
1	FORK	2
NO	PART	OFF

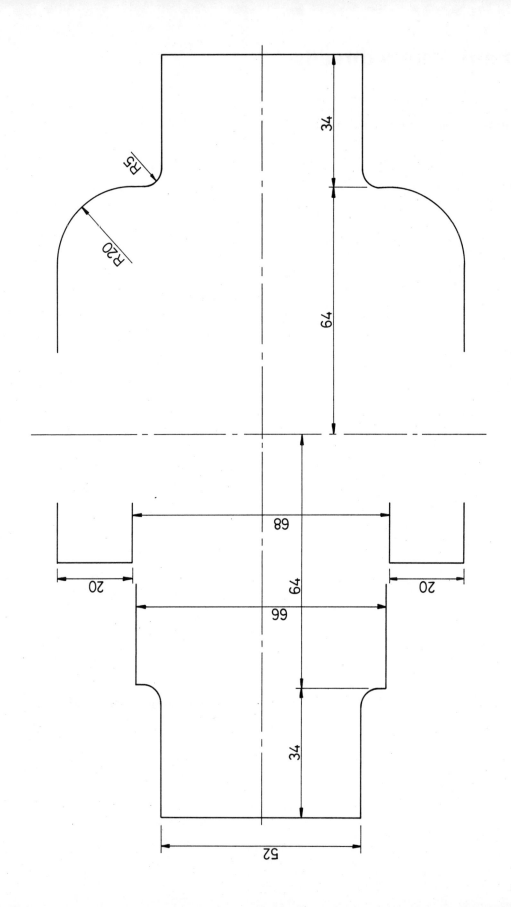

ISO metric screw threads

Part 1 of the British Standard BS:3643 *Specification for ISO metric screw threads* shows two series of ISO metric threads, one with a coarse pitch, the second with a fine pitch.

When dimensioning ISO metric screw threads BS:3643 recommends that the capital letter M be placed before a figure denoting the nominal diameter of the thread in millimetres, and that this is followed by a figure denoting the pitch of the thread in millimetres. Thus a fine series thread of 12 mm diameter would be dimensioned M12 × 1.25, a coarse series thread of 12 mm diameter would be dimensioned M12 × 1.75.

Drawings showing this form of dimensioning ISO metric screw threads are shown in Book 2.

The absence of a pitch number from a thread dimension means that the thread is a coarse series thread. Thus M12 indicates a coarse series thread of pitch 1.75 mm.

Some commonly used coarse series ISO metric screw thread pitches are:

M3 – Pitch 0.5 mm
M4 – Pitch 0.7 mm
M5 – Pitch 0.8 mm
M6 – Pitch 1.0 mm
M8 – Pitch 1.25 mm
M10 – Pitch 1.5 mm
M12 – Pitch 1.75 mm
M16 – Pitch 2.0 mm
M20 – Pitch 2.5 mm
M24 – Pitch 3.0 mm

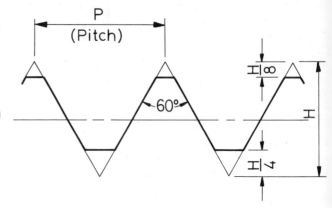

Basic form of ISO metric thread

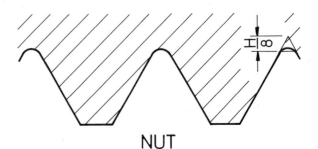

NUT

Design form of internal ISO metric thread

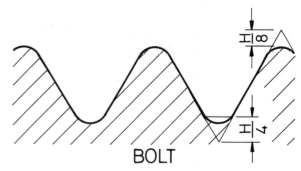

BOLT

Design form of external ISO metric thread

List of abbreviations used on drawings

Across flats	A/F	Maximum	MAX
British Standard	BS	Metre	m
Centimetre (not a recommended SI unit)	cm	Millimetre	mm
		Minimum	MIN
Centres	CRS	Number	NO.
Centre line	CL or ℄	Pitch circle diameter	PCD
Chamfered	CHAM	Radius (preceding dimension)	R
Cheese head	CH HD	Revolutions per minute	RPM
Countersunk	CSK	Right-hand	RH
Countersunk head	CSK HD	Round head	RD HD
Counterbore	C'BORE	Screwed	SCR
Cylinder or cylindrical	CYL	Specification	SPEC
Degree (of angle)	°	Spherical (preceding dimension)	SPHERE Ø
Diameter (in a note)	DIA	Spotface	S'FACE
Diameter (preceding dimension)	Ø	Square (preceding dimension)	□
Drawing	DRG	Square metre	m²
Figure	FIG.	Square millimetre	mm²
Galvanised	GALV	Standard	STD
Hexagon head	HEX HD	Standard Wire Gauge	SWG
International Standards Organization	ISO	Système International d'Unités	SI
Kilogramme	kg	Volume	VOL
Kilometre	km	Weight	WT
Left-hand	LH		

Note: When the abbreviation forms a word, such as FIG. for 'figure', a full stop should follow the abbreviation. Otherwise no full stop should be used.